Piercing the Pennines

Heroic railways linking Lancashire and Yorkshire

David Joy

GREAT NORTHERN

Great Northern Books
PO Box 1380, Bradford,
West Yorkshire, BD5 5FB

www.greatnorthernbooks.co.uk

© David Joy 2021

Uncredited illustrations from the author's collection.

ISBN: 978-1-914227-02-8

Design by David Burrill

CIP Data
A catalogue for this book is available from the British Library

Contents

Totley – longest of all the trans-Pennine tunnels at over 3½ miles. Class 2P 4-4-0 No. 382 is entering the west portal in LMS days. (D Ibbotson)

Introduction

It might seem close to treachery for a dedicated Yorkshireman to write a book giving so much emphasis to Lancashire in general and Manchester in particular. It has to be confessed that the original intention was to celebrate how true Yorkshire grit created heroic railway tunnels linking God's Own County with the other side of the Pennines. Truth to tell, it is the opposite way round. The kick-start and the initial driving force came from Manchester.

The railway tunnels can only be fully appreciated in the context of what came before them. Hence the opening chapter sets the scene by looking first at the remarkable 3rd Duke of Bridgewater, who successfully developed an amazing network of tunnels at his mines near Manchester and then used boats to extract the coal. It paved the way for him to complete a pioneer canal continuing to the Mersey estuary near Liverpool.

Linked with sea-going trade, Manchester surged ahead and was at the centre of numerous proposals to build more canals. It remained cut off from Yorkshire by the Pennines but it was not long before thoughts turned to tunnelling through the barrier. At first the routes were indirect and the tunnels relatively short until work started in 1796 on a bore over three miles long at Standedge. Forming a direct link with Huddersfield and hence existing waterways to Leeds and Hull,

it took fifteen years to complete.

By the time Britain's highest and longest canal tunnel saw its first barge it was close to the dawn of the railway age. It showed what could be achieved but its limitations were only too clear. In the days of proper winters, a big freeze on top of the Pennines could last for weeks and all travel became impossible. Little wonder that there was a big push for railways in the northern hills as soon as they became feasible.

As outlined in the second chapter, they were at first confined to the plains with the successful opening of the landmark Liverpool & Manchester Railway in 1830. Several lines now followed with tunnels of modest length, although passengers were often petrified at the prospect of travelling through them.

A wave of national railway promotion in the mid-1830s brought with it the first of four heroic railways and their tunnels that were eventually to pierce the Pennine watershed. They have radically different features and each one therefore has a separate chapter in this book. Expanding prodigiously and keen to repeat its success in the canal age, Manchester was first in the field.

Inaugurated in 1836 and completed in five years, the Manchester & Leeds Railway with its Summit tunnel had George Stephenson as its engineer. Immortalised as the 'Father of Railways', he insisted that lines must adopt

Pennine tunnels personified at Standedge in a characteristic moorland setting of farmsteads and drystone walls. At bottom right is the Huddersfield Canal, which curves round past the keeper's cottage to enter the earliest and longest of the four tunnels, completed in 1811 after a 15-year struggle. The goods train is about to enter the second railway tunnel of 1871. Smoke is still emerging from the first railway tunnel of 1849 following the passage of an earlier train. To its right is the final double-track tunnel of 1894. Running across the centre of the picture is the then main road from Leeds to Manchester, carrying relatively little traffic in days long before the M62. This evocative photograph was taken some 80 years ago. (Pendragon collection)

minimum gradients to suit locomotives of the day. Rather than just passengers, a prime purpose was to carry freight – and especially coal. The result was an indirect route close to existing canals. As well as the tunnels, this book looks at key settlements served by the new trans-Pennine railways, although in this case there were few of them. Stephenson decided to ignore many towns in order to adhere to his firm policy on gradients and left Oldham, Halifax, Huddersfield and Dewsbury without a direct rail link.

Started a year later was a line where the main driving force was on the Yorkshire side of the Pennines. Canals never managed to penetrate the mountain barrier between Sheffield and Manchester and hence the 'city of steel' felt it was being left behind in the transport revolution. It took the adventurous step of promoting a line climbing high before reaching a tunnel over three miles in length at Woodhead. The mere name was destined to have a dark reputation, as shortages of money meant those heroically toiling to build it were housed in conditions so deplorable that a major row culminated in a parliamentary enquiry. After eight difficult years another famous engineer, Joseph Locke, completed a single-track tunnel in 1845. Such was the volume of traffic that work on a second tunnel had to start within two years.

A factor in delays at Woodhead was an unparalleled depression of trade in the early 1840s, which in turn gave way to the exact opposite. An improving economy, coupled with emergence of the modern stock market and increasing numbers of newspapers, led to promotion of railways as 'foolproof' investments. By 1845 it was the height of the 'railway mania' when almost 3,000 miles of line were sanctioned by Parliament in this chaotic single year. Among them was a more direct route from Leeds to Manchester that would also serve two towns bypassed by Stephenson. One was Dewsbury and the second was Huddersfield, which played a fundamental role in creating a magnificent station façade that has few equals. Often portrayed as a celebration of improved relations between two hitherto hostile railway companies, it had more to do with grandiose ambitions by the Ramsden family as owners of the whole town.

Beyond Huddersfield, the new direct Leeds to Manchester route passed through the Pennine chain by running alongside the existing canal tunnel at Standedge, which was used to extract spoil from the excavations. This saved both cost and time with the result that it was finished in less than three years. In common with the two previous railway tunnels through the Pennines, it was the longest in the world at the time of completion but did not quite exceed the length of that on the canal.

Vital statistics of the tunnels are given in the table on page 8, which seeks to avoid the text becoming too cluttered with dates. Almost all railway companies required sanction by Parliament and the table also shows when those building the tunnels were incorporated and how they subsequently lost or changed their identity.

The 'railway mania' proved short-lived. By 1847 the financial bubble was deflating fast and many speculators lost everything. All three trans-Pennine lines and their tunnels became part of larger concerns as it was the only way they could hope to remain solvent. There was now a desperately needed period of consolidation for railways and their passengers – and also for authors struggling in more recent times to untangle these momentous years of frenzy.

Had Britain's rail system been developed with any sense of central directive there might now have been no need for any further lines. Instead, a spirit of free-for-all competition ensured that many were still constructed with varying degrees of success. A prime example was provided by the Midland Railway, which started off as a provincial company based in Derby and then gradually expanded to reach both London and Carlisle. A direct line belatedly served Sheffield from 1870 but another 24 years elapsed before opening of a link through the Pennines to Manchester. Using the Hope Valley, it involved the separate Totley and Cowburn tunnels.

This was not the end of new tunnels on lines between Sheffield and Manchester. After some one hundred years of suffering fumes and smoke from hard-working steam locomotives, the twin bores at Woodhead were in an appalling state. Work started in 1948 on an impressive double-track tunnel, which would never see regular steam workings as it was an essential part of an electrification scheme. It was a proud moment when it opened in 1954, but a sorrowful occasion when passenger services ceased using it sixteen years later. Complete closure in 1981 left an empty tunnel, which with forward planning could have formed part of a high-speed trans-Pennine line. As it is, commuters between Sheffield and Manchester are faced

Tunnels through the Pennines

CANALS

Foulridge

Leeds & Liverpool Canal

Opened 1st May 1796

1,640 yards [1.49km]

Standedge

Huddersfield Canal

Opened 4th April 1811

3 miles 165 yards [4.98km]; extended in 1894 to 3 miles 418 yards [5.21km]

RAILWAYS

Summit

Manchester & Leeds Railway (incorporated 4th July 1836; became Lancashire & Yorkshire Railway 9th July 1847)

I mile 1125 yards [2.63km]

Double track

Opened 1st March 1841

Woodhead

Sheffield, Ashton-under-Lyne & Manchester Railway (incorporated 5th May 1837; merged to form Manchester, Sheffield & Lincolnshire Railway 27th July 1846; became Great Central Railway 1st August 1897)

3 miles 22 yards [4.85km]

Single track

Opened 23rd December 1845

Second single-track tunnel opened 2nd February 1852.

Both closed on opening of new 3 miles 66 yards [4.89km] double-track tunnel 3rd June 1954 (closed to passengers 5th January 1970 and freight 20th July 1981)

Standedge

Huddersfield & Manchester Railway & Canal Company (incorporated 21st July 1845; absorbed by London & North Western Railway 9th July 1847)

3 miles 62 yards [4.89km]

Single track

Opened 1st August 1849

Second single-track tunnel opened 12th February 1871

Double-track tunnel opened 5th August 1894

Both single-track tunnels closed 31st October 1966

Totley and Cowburn

Dore & Chinley Railway (incorporated 28th July 1884; amalgamated with Midland Railway 24th July 1888)

3 miles 950 yards [5.69 km] and 2 miles 182 yards [3.37km]

Double track

Opened 1st June 1894

The Grouping of railways on 1st January 1923 saw the Great Central absorbed into the London & North Eastern Railway (LNER), with the other companies listed above forming part of the London, Midland & Scottish Railway (LMS). This arrangement continued until the creation of the state-owned British Railways on 1st January 1948.

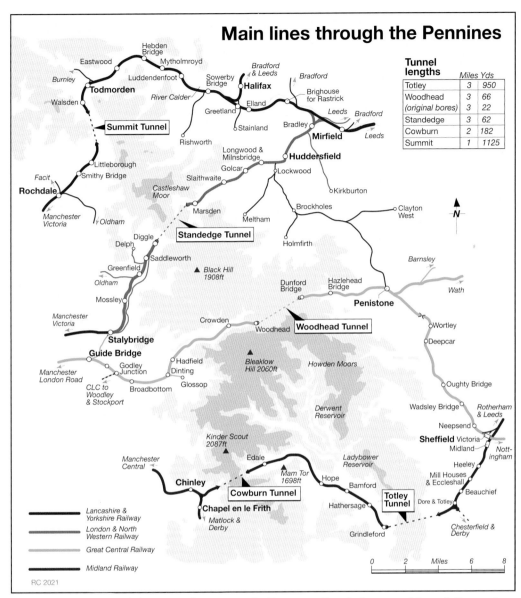

Main lines through the Pennines

Tunnel lengths	Miles	Yds
Totley	3	950
Woodhead (original bores)	3	66
	3	22
Standedge	3	62
Cowburn	2	182
Summit	1	1125

Eastwood · Hebden Bridge · Mytholmroyd · Bradford & Leeds · Bradford
Burnley · Luddendenfoot · Sowerby Bridge · Halifax · Brighouse for Rastrick
Todmorden · River Calder · Elland · Leeds · Bradford
Walsden · Greetland · Stainland · Bradley · Mirfield · Leeds
Summit Tunnel · Rishworth · Longwood & Milnsbridge · Huddersfield
Littleborough · Golcar · Lockwood · Kirkburton
Facit · Smithy Bridge · Slaithwaite · Castleshaw Moor
Rochdale · Marsden · Brockholes · Clayton West
Manchester Victoria · Oldham · Meltham · Standedge Tunnel
Diggle · Holmfirth
Delph · ▲ Black Hill 1908ft · Barnsley
Greenfield · Saddleworth · Dunford Bridge · Hazlehead Bridge · Wath
Oldham · Penistone
Mossley · Crowden · Woodhead · Woodhead Tunnel · Wortley
Manchester Victoria · Deepcar
Stalybridge
Guide Bridge · Hadfield · Bleaklow Hill 2060ft · Howden Moors · Oughty Bridge
Manchester London Road · Godley Junction · Dinting · Wadsley Bridge · Rotherham & Leeds
CLC to Woodley & Stockport · Broadbottom · Glossop · Derwent Reservoir · Neepsend
Kinder Scout 2087ft · Sheffield Victoria / Midland · Nottingham
Manchester Central · Edale · Ladybower Reservoir · Heeley
Chinley · Mam Tor 1698ft · Hope · Mill Houses & Eccleshall · Beauchief
Cowburn Tunnel · Bamford · Totley Tunnel · Dore & Totley
Chapel en le Frith · Hathersage · Chesterfield & Derby
Matlock & Derby · Grindleford

N

Lancashire & Yorkshire Railway
London & North Western Railway
Great Central Railway
Midland Railway

0 2 Miles 6 8

RC 2021

The four main lines and their tunnels piercing the Pennines. For clarity, several branch line stations are omitted, as are the approaches to Manchester and Leeds. (Map by Roger Carvell)

with a slow journey via the Hope Valley or an often more frustrating drive between two cities that still do not have a motorway link.

++++

This book has been written in the form of a continuous narrative for the general reader.

Presenting complexities of the 'railway mania' in digestible form is challenging enough and the history of lines in the main centres of Manchester, Leeds and Sheffield would be even more demanding. Coverage has not been attempted in these pages and historians requiring more detailed information are directed to Sources and Further Reading on page 122.

Some explanation is required. The map was specially drawn for this book to save hundreds of words that could become tedious. It is primarily intended to give a broad perspective, with emphasis on the high ground that necessitated the tunnels. It shows the companies operating the main lines prior to the Grouping of railways in 1923.

County boundaries are omitted, as this is an especially difficult area where a careless mistake can ignite lingering discontent going back to the Wars of the Roses. All the trans-Pennine lines covered in this book were built to link Lancashire with Yorkshire – or vice-versa according to one's viewpoint! This does not necessarily apply to the location of their tunnels. For example, Summit was entirely in Lancashire until boundary changes in 1888 placed part of it in Yorkshire's West Riding – an enormous area stretching well across the

watershed almost to the centre of Oldham. Similarly, Standedge tunnel was wholly in Yorkshire until 1974, when abolition of the Ridings caused deep dismay east of the Pennines. The wounds have gradually healed but it is a subject where extreme diplomacy is still needed.

As regards terminology, it is sometimes forgotten that the description 'Pennines' was not in common use until well into the nineteenth century. It is derived from the Apennines in Italy, similarly running down the spine of the country, and superseded the wordy 'England's mountain chain'. Elsewhere in print, much confusion often arises between 'carriages' and 'coaches' – a safe definition is that the former run on rails and the latter on roads.

Unless otherwise stated, opening and closure dates in the text relate solely to passenger services and not goods traffic.

Metrication in Britain has become as ambivalent as its relationship with Europe, but metric equivalents are included for most heights, dimensions and distances. They are generally omitted where the distance is less than ten miles, as this frequently occurs and constant repetition would be tedious.

A final point concerns money. To state that something cost say £500 in 1850 does not convey a great deal in present-day terms. All monetary values therefore include today's figure based on the percentage increase in the Retail Price Index. This is a controversial area and it cannot be stressed too highly that it is no more than an approximate indication.

1

Industrial Revolution

Canal Age to Railway Age

Calder & Hebble Navigation near Elland

The Canal Age

Lancashire and the West Riding of Yorkshire led Britain and the world into the industrial revolution. Yet they were long cut off from one another by a great mountain chain. The Pennines, stretching north from Derbyshire to the Tyne Gap, have often been termed 'the backbone of England' and have precious few points where the watershed is below the 1,000ft [310m] contour. They are notable for water rushing down from the hills in innumerable streams, becks and small rivers. It is soft and lime-free and proved ideal for cleansing the wool from sheep that thrive on the upland pastures. Hence fulling mills were established by the streams and a domestic cloth industry developed in hill-top villages from the 13th century.

Among many rivers rising on the steep western slopes of the Pennines is the Irwell, which turns south to head through towns with such richly evocative Lancashire names as Bacup, Rawtenstall, Ramsbottom and Bury. It then enters the plains to flow through the twin settlements of Salford and Manchester before joining the Mersey. To its last the Irwell remains close to the Pennines and Manchester has the rare distinction of 2,000ft [600m] mountain summits less than 20 miles [32km] from its centre.

In the same distance westwards is Warrington – the main port of the Mersey estuary when Liverpool was still a fishing village. It handled cloth, brought down from the Pennine villages by pack-horses and then transferred to river craft in Manchester, which expanded rapidly and was described by the 16th-century poet John Leland as 'the fairest, best builded, quickest and most populous town of all Lancashire'. River traffic became more dependable when weirs were replaced with locks and acute bends with 'cuts' on formation of the Manchester & Irwell Navigation Company in 1721, but its many meanders still left much to be desired. There was soon to be dramatic change.

Key developments pushing Manchester to the forefront of the industrial revolution centred on canals and then railways. This pioneer aqueduct taking barges across the River Irwell caused a sensation when completed in 1763. (Watercolour by G F Yates)

The Canal Duke

Completion of the Navigation in 1736 coincided with an event in Worsley, five miles north-west of Manchester, which must have seemed of minimal significance. The birth occurred of Francis Egerton, who at the age of eleven inherited the title of the 3rd Duke of Bridgewater. Shortly after attaining his majority he became engaged to the society beauty the Dowager Duchess of Hamilton. It is perhaps as well for the subsequent development of Manchester that the match was broken off and the Duke gave up his London seat to retire to his Worsley estate. He remained a bachelor and devoted the rest of his life to creating canals – a passion engendered when he made the customary aristocratic Grand Tour of Europe and saw the pioneer Canal du Midi in France.

The Duke's achievements were extraordinary, thanks in part to his resident engineer and agent John Gilbert. The ducal coal mines at Worsley were hindered by lack of transport and so the two men created a unique network of underground canals, which in terms of their length vastly exceeded anything later to be seen on railways piercing the Pennines. Eventually totalling an astonishing 46 miles [74 km], the tunnels carried laden boats that were 'legged' by men laying on top of the coal and pushing against the roof or walls with their feet.

The Duke went on to create what is

generally regarded as the first 'proper' canal, fed by an artificial supply of water as opposed to a river navigation dependent on an existing flow. Work had started by 1759 with the initial intention of linking the mines with the Irwell so that the coal could then be transferred to river craft for the final few miles into Manchester. Far from ideal, it was a problem only solved when Gilbert introduced the Duke to James Brindley, a semi-literate millwright who recognised few limitations.

Nicknamed 'the Schemer', he came up with what was seen as a foolhardy plan to take the canal across the Irwell by the first aqueduct in England. With three 40ft [12m] high arches it was viewed with great suspicion until Brindley gave a messy but convincing demonstration in Parliament that the use of puddled clay would make it watertight.

The engineer John Smeaton, who had recently overseen the building of Eddystone lighthouse, commented: 'I have often heard of castles in the air, but never before saw where any of them were to be erected.'

Doubts were cast aside when completion of the canal in 1763 more than halved the price of coal in Manchester. Flushed with its success the Duke now decided on a far more ambitious scheme to extend the waterway for 24 lock-free miles [39km] across the Cheshire plain to Runcorn on the south side of the Mersey estuary. Here the developing port of Liverpool had seen its first dock open in 1715 and would provide convenient transfer with sea-going vessels.

The Duke was convinced he could break the monopoly and hence excessive charges levied by the Mersey & Irwell Navigation Company. He was also determined to avoid hazards and delays on the two rivers, which were always dependent on the amount of water coming down from the hills. Both ambitions were quickly realised on completion of the Bridgewater Canal in 1776.

It was still predominantly an era of horse-hauled barges, but large boats known as 'Mersey flats' had sails that could be used on the completed Bridgewater Canal when wind and direction were favourable. They could carry up to 80 tons. A flourishing service of packet-boats with 1st, 2nd and 3rd Class cabins was established between Manchester and Warrington with respective fares of two shillings and sixpence [£17], one shilling [£6.80] and tenpence [£5.70]. Passenger facilities included ticket and parcels offices as well as waiting rooms.

The debts incurred by the Duke peaked at an alarming £346,000 [£45 million] in 1786 and he came close to bankruptcy, but the enterprise was soon making a huge profit. Canals became the arteries of the industrial revolution with obvious advantages over the then apology for roads and many miles of new waterways played a fundamental role in tunnels that pierced the Pennines.

Driving canal tunnels through high ground could pose massive difficulties, just as was later to be the case in the railway age. Opening of the full length of the Trent & Mersey Canal, engineered by James Brindley, was delayed by some six years pending completion of Harecastle tunnel. Its north portal is in the centre of this picture, with its later successor by Thomas Telford on the left. (Akke Monasso)

Pioneer challenge

Once work was under way to link Manchester with sea-going trade through Liverpool, the next goal was an inland waterway across England to the equivalent East Coast port of Hull. It might have long remained in the realms of fantasy had it not been for the Trent, Britain's third-longest river, which rises on the Staffordshire moors less than 20 miles [32km] distant from the Mersey but then perversely heads south in a giant 'U', skirting the lower flanks of the Pennines through Stoke-on-Trent and Nottingham before finally reaching the Humber estuary. The Trent & Mersey Canal, linking the Bridgewater near Runcorn with the navigable headwaters of the river, therefore made eminent sense.

Sanctioned by Parliament in 1766, it was almost 100 miles in length and by a remarkable achievement was largely completed in five years. The one short remaining section, taking twice as long, was the 1 mile 1,120yd [2.63km] summit tunnel at Harecastle. In passing through a southern outlier of the Pennines it may not have linked Lancashire with Yorkshire but it was then the longest canal tunnel in the country and certainly provided a foretaste of future challenges.

Fifteen vertical shafts were sunk down from the surface and the canal line was then formed by mining outwards from the bottom of each shaft. The work was undertaken by navvies – an abridgement of the word 'navigators'. According to one hellfire chaplain, the term arose because in full it sounded too similar to 'alligators'. He held that a navvy was akin to a human alligator, who feeds on helpless women and timid men, and frightens children into fits!

Pumps had to be provided to prevent flooding and stoves installed at the bottom of pipes to overcome ventilation problems. It was an anxious time for James Brindley, who was again the engineer, and also for Josiah Wedgwood, who backed the canal as an outlet for his potteries at Stoke. During this period the pots had to be carried from one end of the tunnel to the other by horse, no doubt in earnest hope that breakages would be kept to a minimum!

The tunnel did not have a towpath and, as at Worsley coal mines, barges had to be 'legged' through by men pushing against the roof or walls with their feet. It was slow and hard work with travel time averaging three hours. While this was taking place, the tow-horses – often led by boat children – were taken over the hill above the tunnel.

Brindley died in 1772 before completion of Harecastle tunnel. By the 1820s it had become a major bottleneck due to the slow process of 'legging' and it was augmented by a second tunnel built by the noted Scottish civil engineer Thomas Telford. Constructed in only three years due to advances in civil engineering, the provision of a towpath meant that horses could now pull boats through in a much shorter time.

King Cotton

Opening of the full length of the Trent & Mersey in 1777 created the first inland waterway between the Irish Sea and the North Sea. Even though it had to skirt round rather than go through the Pennine backbone, with journeys measured in days rather than hours, it was still a vast improvement in moving goods across the country. Its link near Runcorn with the Bridgewater Canal put Manchester on waterways not just to Liverpool and Hull but also Birmingham and hence Bristol via the Severn. The springboard was now set for radical change on a grand scale.

Manchester was in an unassailable position when a sudden and incessant demand for one specific fibre transformed Lancashire from a little known corner of Britain into the industrial centre of the world. Raw cotton had long been expensively imported in small quantities from the Middle East to Norwich where it was used in making fustian – a heavy cloth mainly worn by men. It was then found that the cotton could best be washed in the damp and rainy conditions of the Pennines, leading to a decline in the traditional activity of making coarse woollen fabrics. In dimly lit and draughty dwellings, whole families combined farming with spinning and weaving. Infants learned to strip seeds from the washed cotton, which their elder siblings carded and passed to the spinsters before the yarns were woven on the handloom. It was a laborious process.

Change came through native genius and a remarkable sequence of inventions by Lancashire men rising from the humblest of beginnings. Bury-born John Kay invented the 'fly-shuttle', so named because of its continuous speed, which doubled weaving productivity. Achieving the same rapidity with cotton spinning was more of a challenge, so there matters rested until the heady days of Georgian England. Ladies of the aristocracy began purchasing clothes for style rather than necessity and voluminous cotton dresses together with huge bonnets became the height of fashion.

Supply could not remotely meet demand and one of the greatest technical challenges of the age was how to substitute a machine for fingers worked almost to breaking point on the domestic hand-wheel. James Hargreaves, an Oswaldtwistle weaver and carpenter, helped to meet this need by inventing the 'spinning jenny'. The number of threads that could be spun in a single operation was increased but there were still limitations.

The real breakthrough occurred when Richard Arkwright, born in Preston as the thirteenth son of a tailor, eked out a living by buying human hair to make wigs. On his travels he would hear spinners bemoaning the want of a way to keep pace with Kay's weaving shuttle. Suitably inspired, he teamed up with a local watchmaker to perfect a machine that substituted wooden and metal cylinders for fingers and could spin well over a hundred threads at a time. These were stronger than those twisted by hand on a wheel and a single technical advance capable of working round the clock now heralded a new age in manufacturing. Before he was 40 he had opened the famous Cromford Mill alongside the River Derwent in Derbyshire.

In 1779 Arkwright built a pioneer steam-driven textile mill in Manchester and turned cotton into a readily available yarn. Knighted by George III, he became known as the 'father of the modern industrial factory'. Further progress in this saga occurred when Bolton-born Samuel Crompton invented the 'spinning mule', which could easily be installed by any small manufacturer with basic confidence and minimal capital.

Nothing could now stop Manchester. Condemnation that raw cotton brought into Liverpool from the West Indies and the southern states of America formed part of the slave trade was far in the future. For the moment it was sufficient that it could readily be transhipped to craft on the Bridgewater Canal and close on a hundred warehouses were built to receive the material. Barges on the same canal also conveyed coal from the Duke's mines at Worsley, which meant most mills were soon steam-powered thanks to the Scottish inventor James Watt. It mattered not that the town was now a grimy place with blackened skies. Families who for generations had been spinning and weaving in the Pennine hills came down to a new life and brought with them a spirit of enterprise, skill and innovation. The volume of production increased many times over with the result that everybody from the duchess to the mill girl could wear cheaper cotton cloth.

Steam power led to sweeping changes and drew industry into other coal-producing areas such as Oldham and Rochdale, which were soon among the largest cotton-spinning towns in the country. Yet it was Manchester that retained its dominant role as the first centre of mass production fundamentally and irreversibly changing the world.

Challenges in Yorkshire

There could never be an equivalent of Manchester on the eastern flanks of the Pennines. Instead of a sudden descent to the plains, the slopes are much gentler and are intersected by lengthy rivers. The Aire rises in the Yorkshire Dales and wends its way through Skipton and Keighley before entering the Vale of York east of Leeds. More surprising is the Calder, rising within five miles of Burnley but then flowing east through a deep and narrow valley that only broadens out near Halifax. The river passes close to Huddersfield and Dewsbury before in turn reaching the plain at Wakefield and joining the Aire at Castleford.

Upland pastures – and hence flocks of sheep – on the slopes of the Yorkshire Pennines were far in excess of the numbers in Lancashire. At first it seemed the West Riding would surge ahead when the Aire & Calder Navigation became the first successful inland waterway to be promoted by merchants and industrialists rather than land-owning aristocracy. It was brought into use in 1701 a good thirty years prior to completion of its Manchester & Irwell equivalent. Both Leeds and Wakefield were now linked with Goole and hence Hull, and it might have been expected that they would soon form one single centre to handle large quantities of woven cloth brought down from the hills. Even though they are only ten miles apart, it did not happen.

The wool trade expanded over a huge area stretching westwards and embraced many small towns, but it may have been the individual nature of Yorkshiremen that caused each settlement to cling tenaciously to its own ideals and independence. There was neither a presiding genius akin to the Duke of Bridgewater nor a succession of gifted inventors to transform transport and textiles.

In any event there were two fundamental limitations. Basic geography meant there was no way the West Riding could erode the supremacy in cotton production enjoyed by Lancashire, which could so easily import the raw material from America through Liverpool. Moreover, wool could not withstand the harshness of early mechanisation in the same way as cotton fibres and therefore hand-spinning and weaving remained to the fore.

Halifax had for centuries been a dominant centre for woollen merchants but they became increasingly envious of the cheap water transport enjoyed by competitors in Wakefield at the upper limit of the Aire & Calder Navigation. After many setbacks the river was improved westwards as far as Sowerby Bridge on the edge of Halifax, where Hebble Brook flowed through the town centre. It accordingly gave its name to the Calder & Hebble Navigation, completed in 1774. Two years later saw opening of the connecting four-mile Sir John Ramsden's Canal into Huddersfield named after the local worthy who claimed to own every house in the town except one.

The key centres of Leeds, Wakefield, Huddersfield and Halifax now all had water-borne transport to Hull, but left out on its own was Bradford. Although then only a small town it also had an important cloth market and a group of its merchants were convinced by Halifax engineer John Longbottom to back a truly ambitious project. In 1770 Parliament authorised what at 127 miles [204 km] was eventually to be Britain's longest single canal. The Leeds & Liverpool also had the more unfortunate record of being the most protracted to be built.

As the first trans-Pennine canal directly to link Lancashire and Yorkshire, there are bound to be suspicions that a fundamental problem was age-old feuding between the two counties. Certainly, there were initially what might be termed strong differences of opinion between its two supporting committees –

The Leeds & Liverpool Canal used the lowest of all Pennine crossings but still needed this tunnel almost a mile long at Foulridge. It was a cost the railway managed to avoid when taking the same route between Skipton and the Lancashire textile towns in 1848. (John Slater)

one in Lancashire based in Liverpool and one in Yorkshire meeting in Bradford and controlling the finances. Liverpudlians at one stage threatened to wreck the project before it even started.

Progress should not have been too demanding, largely because the canal was able to use the Aire Gap – at under 500ft [150m] the lowest of all trans-Pennine crossings between the two counties. Yet by 1777, the year that saw Manchester and Liverpool linked with Hull by the Trent & Mersey, there was still an interminably long haul ahead for Bradford merchants to achieve their vision

of 'a waterway to unite the seas'. The canal had been completed from the Aire & Calder Navigation in Leeds through to Shipley, where it was joined by an all-important short branch from Bradford. From here the main artery continued through Keighley and Skipton to a wharf at the small settlement of Gargrave. Endless financial problems and disputes over the route to be followed in Lancashire then delayed matters for almost another four decades. It was not until 1816 that a grand flotilla of boats sailed the entire length of the canal through to Liverpool to celebrate the end of 46 years' work.

Another tunnel

Unlike the Trent & Mersey, it was thus local politics rather than the summit tunnel that long deferred the grand opening. Even though it was much shorter, the 1,640yd [1.49 km] Foulridge tunnel nevertheless posed plenty of problems and proved to be appropriately named. When work finally began early in 1791, it was soon found that much of the ground was unstable sand and steam engines had to be erected to pump away surplus water.

The Scottish engineer John Rennie was called in to inspect operations and recorded in his notebook: 'Only 700 yards could be worked underground; the remainder was obliged to be worked from above ... The sides of the excavation were supported by timber, at an immense labour and expense, to prevent the earth falling in, until the tunnel arch was constructed.'

He was referring to what today is known as the cut-and-cover system, whereby the ground is first excavated prior to erection of the tunnel lining and replacement of the earth. The work proved difficult and dangerous, and it seems likely that collapse of the supporting framework in August 1791 was the cause of four workers receiving either one guinea [£182] or half a guinea according to the nature of their injuries. The surgeon's bill of one guinea was also paid by the company, which became directly involved with construction when the private contractor gave up in 1792.

Despite operations continuing night and day, a further four years elapsed before the work was finally completed. As at Harecastle, there was no towpath and barges were 'legged' through the tunnel. A hut was provided above the western portal for professional leggers and a good track created through the fields so that horses could be led over the top.

The Rochdale Canal

Construction of Foulridge tunnel coincided with what became known as the 'canal mania' of the early 1790s and a desire to complete an obvious gap in the network of northern waterways. Moving goods from Manchester to the main centres of the industrial West Riding was still largely by pack-horse. Otherwise it was a great way round and involved all points of the compass. A patient bargee would first have to head west along the Bridgewater Canal to Runcorn and then south, east and north via Stoke, Nottingham and the Humber estuary before again swinging west up the Aire & Calder Navigation. The lengthy journey of several days must at times have seemed tedious in the extreme, made worse by the knowledge that the straight-line distance from Manchester to waterways at either Sowerby Bridge or Huddersfield was little more than 20 miles [32km].

The Pennine chain was still a major obstacle both technically and financially, but determination was mounting. After considerable hesitation, two rival schemes were approved by Parliament on the same day in April 1794. One was a great success, one a near failure, and both played a key part in the railway age that was less than 30 years into the future.

The Rochdale Canal owed much of its success to a fortunate accident of physical geography. South of the Aire Gap, one of the few low-lying crossings of the Pennines is provided by Walsden Gorge – a glacial meltwater channel extending from near

Unlike the Leeds & Liverpool and later railways, the Rochdale Canal crossed the Pennine watershed without a tunnel. It is seen here in the narrow valley between Todmorden and Hebden Bridge with the River Calder, the main road and the railway all to its left but scarcely visible among the woodland. (Tim Green of Bradford)

Littleborough to the River Calder at Todmorden. Although forming a route not noted for its directness, it avoids the worst of the weather on the Pennine heights and was an obvious choice for a canal that would pass through Rochdale in linking Manchester with the head of the Calder & Hebble Navigation at Sowerby Bridge.

Its supporters were fortunate in engaging the services of William Jessop, a leading engineer of his day who had already built the Grand Canal of Ireland. His main challenge was how to go through Walsden Gorge, which despite all its advantages still required a summit pound 610ft [183m] above sea level. Jessop could have opted for tunnelling, but it was not an approach he favoured. He argued that having more locks and thus bringing a canal more quickly into revenue-earning use could reduce the expense and extra time in boring a summit tunnel. It was

a principle that may not always have been viewed with favour by generations of boat owners, as there was a grand total of 93 locks in the overall length of just 33 miles [53km]. Perhaps that is why the textile village at the top formerly known as Calderbrook assumed the name of Summit, as reaching it must often have seemed the pinnacle of achievement for many a weary user.

Despite this economy the Rochdale Canal had cost over £600,000 [£53 million] by the time it opened in 1804. It was built in the grand manner with massive locks that could take vessels of 14ft [4.2m] width. In a wonderful instance of the transport revolution, 'Mersey flats' returning from Ireland under sail would have their masts dismantled on entering the Bridgewater Canal and would then be hauled by horses all the way to Sowerby Bridge.

Soon the main highway of commerce between Lancashire and Yorkshire, the

Rochdale transported a huge variety of merchandise with coal, grain and wool by far the largest consignments. Timber came through Hull for the long haul to the west and the same port handled finished goods for shipment to London and the continent. Corn came from Gainsborough and Lincoln to feed Lancashire mill workers as did flour, malt and bran. Eyebrows would today no doubt be raised when the same boats returned with street sweepings, stable dung and nightsoil from Manchester.

The Rochdale Canal also changed the industrial landscape of Calderdale with increasing numbers of cotton mills in such towns as Todmorden and Hebden Bridge. Sited alongside the waterway, they could easily receive supplies of coal and dispatch their products. It was a sad time in the 1960s when the canal largely became derelict and a triumphant moment when in 2002 it was reopened for navigation along its entire length.

Huddersfield Canal

Part of their undoing was that canals in Britain largely divided into two categories – 'broad' such as the Rochdale and Sir John Ramsden's canals able to take a 14ft [4.2m] barge and 'narrow' where construction costs and water usage were saved with dimensions restricted to craft only 6ft 10in [2.05m] wide. Where the two met, as happened in Huddersfield, there were often delays and extra costs due to transhipment.

Whether the 'narrow' Huddersfield Canal should have been built at all is arguable. Twenty miles [32km] in length, it connected with the Ashton Canal east of Manchester to form a waterway to Huddersfield half the distance of that via the Rochdale Canal and the Calder & Hebble Navigation. It proved to be a shortcut only achieved through inordinate cost and delay. In spite of all the problems posed by the summit tunnels at Harecastle and Foulridge, it was decided to go for broke. There was no Walsden Gorge to help and the only way was straight through the Pennine watershed. Nothing quite so stubbornly optimistic had been seen as the 3 miles 165yd [4.98km] of Britain's longest and highest canal tunnel at Standedge, 648ft [194m] above sea level and 636ft [191m] below moorland at its deepest point. It was reached by passing through 32 locks up the Tamar Valley to Diggle before eventually emerging into the Colne Valley and a descent of 42 locks into Huddersfield.

Considering what lay ahead, all at first went surprisingly well and 15 miles [24km] of the canal were soon completed. Yet it was not long before the great tunnel began to overshadow all other progress. It seems the original intention of consulting engineer Benjamin Outram was to adopt the same approach as at Harecastle, tunnelling not only from each end but also from the foot of vertical shafts sunk from the bleak moor top, using pumps to get rid of surplus water. A mid-1796 report describes preparations for building nine waterwheels to raise water or spoil, with 1,485yd [1.35km] of subsidiary runnels having been driven to drain surface springs. Fourteen shafts were finished or in progress and one large and three small steam engines had been installed in an attempt to keep the works free from flooding during construction. Only 791yd [237m] of tunnel had been cut.

By autumn 1796 it was clear just how many difficulties had to be overcome. In November one shaft was being sunk at only a yard a week. Soon afterwards Outram decided to limit tunnelling solely from the outer ends, using the shafts and header tunnels for pumping the surfeit of water and raising spoil. The decision saved costs but greatly increased delay before

Britain's highest, longest and most expensive canal tunnel at Standedge was finally opened in 1811 and greatly helped construction of the parallel main-line railway from Huddersfield to Manchester. This view from the front of a boat captures what seems a passage of eternal gloom. (Wikimedia)

the tunnel could be finished. Money was running out by early 1799. Costs had been seriously underestimated and a large sum was owed from shareholders, some of whom were bankrupt, while others were dead or had left the country. A committee agreed that in order to raise funds each of its members should 'use their utmost endeavours by personally waiting upon Gentlemen'.

Matters went from bad to worse and a surveyor's report in late 1800 found faulty construction and incorrect levels to the extent that much of the arching had to be taken down and rebuilt. It did not help that Outram had many other commitments and was far from easy for those working with him. He had bouts of serious illness and in 1805 died from what was described as 'brain fever'. In a barbed tribute, his wife Margaret wrote that he was 'hasty in his temper, feeling his own superiority over others. Accustomed to command, he had little toleration for stupidity and slowness, and none for meanness or littleness of any kind.'

The Scottish engineer Thomas Telford was now called in for advice, but there was no escaping the fact that completing a tunnel of this length was bound to be protracted. The work continued relentlessly week-by-week

and month-by-month, and not until June 1809 were the two ends finally joined. Almost another two years elapsed before enlarging and lining the bore permitted a ceremonial opening on 4th April 1811, watched by a crowd gathered at the Diggle entrance and estimated at 10,000 strong. The strains of 'Rule Britannia' then rent the moorland air as a party of 500 disappeared into the tunnel on several loaded boats and emerged at the Huddersfield end almost two hours later.

What was by far the most expensive canal tunnel ever built in Britain at a cost of £160,000 [£11.7 million] was finally finished but it was scarcely a moment of triumph. The Rochdale Canal had now been open for seven years and had cornered most of the available traffic. There were also what today would be termed serious operational difficulties. Thoughts of providing a towpath had been abandoned, as shareholders could not face further delay and expense. 'Legging' underground over this distance took so long that it proved impractical and one-way working had to be introduced with boats going through in convoy. It damaged the competitiveness of the whole enterprise and the Huddersfield Canal proved to be the least successful of all trans-Pennine waterways.

The Railway Age

The long delayed completion of the Leeds & Liverpool and Huddersfield canals coincided with a new era in the industrial and transport revolution. In 1804 the gifted Cornish engineer Richard Trevithick had succeeded in building the first high-pressure steam locomotive, which managed to haul five wagons containing ten tons of iron and 70 people at the then sensational speed of five miles per hour. Eight years later, Leeds had the first commercially successful railway in the world when John Blenkinsop put locomotives to work on a line from Middleton Colliery down to the River Aire.

George Stephenson, a self-educated engineman at Killingworth Colliery on Tyneside, now turned crude colliery engines into a revolutionary means of public transport. The 'Father of Railways' was instrumental in creating the Stockton & Darlington Railway, opened in 1825 and soon saddled with many spurious claims to fame. It was neither the first railway nor the first to use steam power. Rather more subtly, it was the first locomotive-worked public railway, although even then there was an alarming throwback to former times. At first only the coal trains were steam-hauled and members of the public with the necessary resources could run their own horse-hauled carriages over the line.

The real breakthrough centred on two

George Stephenson was resident engineer of the Liverpool & Manchester Railway, the first to carry passengers and goods entirely using steam locomotives when opened in 1830. Among his later projects was the Manchester & Leeds Railway – the first line through the Pennines.

towns now symbolic of a new age by expanding at an uncontrollable rate that was also seen as frightening. In just 30 years from 1791 the population of Manchester grew from 57,000 to 134,000 as the cotton industry drew in workers from Scotland, Wales and the rest of England. Liverpool saw the number of its inhabitants more than double in the same period. In 1792 the port handled a modest 500 bags of cotton imported from America but the quantity had reached a phenomenal 412,000 by 1823.

The pioneer canals had been crucial in developing national and international markets but were becoming victims of their own success. The sheer volume of traffic was leading to costly delays and there were also accusations of excessive charges levied by the Marquess of Stafford, who was now proprietor of the Bridgewater Canal. Profiteering was coming full circle.

A group of Liverpool merchants joined forces with cotton men in Manchester to promote what was rightly hailed as a landmark in the technical and economic development of the world. Opened in 1830 with Stephenson as its resident engineer, the Liverpool & Manchester Railway was the first to carry passengers and goods entirely by mechanical traction using steam locomotives over its 31-mile [50km] main line.

It had all the elements that were soon to become familiar in the new railway age – a double-track line of iron rails complete with stations, signals, bridges, cuttings, embankments and a mix of 1st, 2nd and 3rd Class carriages. Prior to opening it had already achieved acclaim when trials held on the Rainhill length of the line proved once and for all the superiority of steam locomotion. The £500 [£44,000] prize was won by Stephenson's *Rocket*. On the opening day it played centre stage in the first accident on a public railway when William Huskisson – leader of a progressive wing of the Tory party – was run over and died close to the line.

Despite this initial setback, the Liverpool & Manchester was a huge success with trains covering the journey in two hours. Passenger receipts in the first year totalled over £100,000 [£9 million] compared with an estimate of £10,000. Steam power had successfully fuelled the industrial revolution and it was now the turn of steam locomotion to transport not just passengers but also bulk supplies of raw materials and finished goods. Above all, it could meet an incessant demand to move vast amounts of coal from mines to mill furnaces and the domestic fireside.

It was sufficient to trigger the first wave of railway construction on a grand scale and create incessant demand for the services of George Stephenson. Just as with canals, a key issue to be addressed and creating fierce divergence of opinion was whether to go round or through the highest ground. The 'Father of Railways', recognising the limitations of early locomotives, had a firm maxim that gradients should be kept to an absolute minimum. He preferred to go round, but where this proved impractical he opted for tunnelling rather than steep inclines. Many early railways thus had tunnels as a noted feature.

Tunnel entrances at Edge Hill, the western end of the Liverpool & Manchester Railway. Cables operating the centre Wapping tunnel down to the docks can be seen in the foreground and were hopefully also clearly visible to ladies, who were expected to descend the steep steps without tripping over their fashionable attire. (Aquatint by Thomas Bury)

Early tunnels

Uncertainty persists on the first tunnel to be used by paying passengers. A little-known claimant was a primitive tourist attraction at East Kenton Colliery, which may have been familiar to Stephenson as it was close to his Tyneside home. Kitty's Drift was in mining terms a horizontal level rather than a vertical shaft. It scarcely matched the later concept of a railway tunnel, but it offered the adventurous a means of visiting a coal mine without being precariously suspended on the end of a rope. A graphic description was given in *Akenhead's Guide to Newcastle*, published in 1807:

'Some of the men will assist in seating you on a set of small, empty coal wagons, capable of carrying two persons each, seven of which are drawn along a railway by one horse. As soon as you are placed, with your candles lighted, you set off at full speed, with a boy in the first wagon, for your charioteer, into a tunnel six feet high, about the same in breadth, and three miles in length ... At your first entrance into this tunnel you are struck with the noise of the wagons, which being fastened with chains to each other, and going at the rate of ten miles an hour, make a reverberating noise resembling thunder.'

The account went on to capture what happened at passing loops when a train of wagons was coming out of the mine: 'The boy stops his horse, and a dead silence ensues, forming a striking contrast to the noise you have just heard. After calling aloud, he listens to hear if any loaded wagons are coming down, that they may pass each other. The candle of the boy coming down appears like a star in the distance, through the gloom, and has a very pleasing effect, as it gradually

Early passengers had a dread of railway tunnels and several were gas lit as happened in Liverpool at Wapping. A previous version of this Thomas Bury aquatint included a locomotive but had to be corrected as steam power was not allowed in a tunnel well over a mile in length.

approaches.'

'Very pleasing' may have been far from the truth for many of the brave passengers. There must have been similar emotions to surviving a ghost train at fairgrounds in more recent times and certainly a horror of railway tunnels never entirely went away.

Tunnels in a more conventional sense were a feature of the Liverpool & Manchester Railway. On its opening, a cutting at Edge Hill had at its western end what appeared to be three separate portals. The single-track on the right led to Liverpool's Crown Street passenger station. The twin bore in the centre was where goods traffic was lowered down to the docks for over a mile on a 1 in 48 incline using cable and a stationary steam engine. The left-hand bore led no further than a store room and in the spirit of the age was provided purely to maintain architectural symmetry.

Operations on early lines were often rudimentary, a prime example being provided by the Leicester & Swannington Railway, promoted in 1830 with Stephenson's son Robert as its engineer. Adhering to canal practice, it had level sections interspersed with short inclines. These replaced the locks on a canal and were cable-worked where the gradient was too steep for a locomotive. Opening of the single-track line in 1832 saw the first train personally driven by George Stephenson. It was fortunately not a more serious incident when the engine had its chimney knocked off inside the 1 mile 9yd [1.61km] Glenfield tunnel owing to the track having been packed up too high. The directors anticipated that only coal traffic would be carried but were able to meet a demand from local passengers by hastily building a carriage. Facilities remained primitive with local inns and tiny huts serving as booking offices.

Also promoted in 1830 and having many

features that now seem quaint was the Leeds & Selby Railway. Trains connected with packet-boats to Hull on the tidal River Ouse and their timings were often uncertain. Its most notable feature was the 700yd [637m] Richmond Hill tunnel, where early travellers were apparently terror-stricken by the thought of a 'steam monster' in its Stygian depths. The company responded by whitewashing the interior and installing sheets of tinned copper at the foot of the air shafts in order to reflect light. It was claimed that a newspaper could be read inside the tunnel.

A reporter from the *Leeds Mercury* experienced mixed feelings of admiration and horror when seeing construction in progress: 'The men who work here seem to possess Herculean strength: their muscles are strongly developed, and the power of their strokes is tremendous. The excavators are generally known to have not the most prepossessing appearance; and their grim countenances, brawny arms, their uncouth labour, the farthing-candle illumination of the hideous pit in which they are digging … combine to render the scene more striking than pleasing.'

He was conveying a way of life that was to go hand-in-hand with ever-longer tunnels as the railway age took a dramatic leap forward.

Men at work

A pattern evolved with a main engineer such as George Stephenson solely and ultimately responsible to the railway company for all that was either being achieved or going dreadfully wrong. Below him a tunnel would have a resident engineer, who knew the importance of a close working relationship with the main contractor. Subordinates were kept to a minimum and there were no fancy job titles such as liaison officers or feasibility assessors.

The workforce provided a direct link with the canal age with men still known as navvies. There could easily be a thousand of them, lured by high wages, and providing daily supplies of food in what was often a remote location could be a real challenge. Navvies had a reputation for consuming two pounds of beef, two pounds of bread and a gallon of beer at a single sitting.

Temporary housing resulted in shanty towns with an appalling stench and fetid waste everywhere. The less impoverished and more caring companies would erect dormitory-type huts, but it was often a case of primitive shelters thrown up by the men and having roofs far from watertight. Grossly overcrowded, they had truckle beds to make maximum use of floor space and any young children were suspended from the roof in baskets. Disease was rife and syphilis commonplace. Navvies had many women but few wives, who would in any event be sold for a gallon of beer. A bizarre marriage ceremony would see the couple jump over a broomstick in a hut full of men gathered to drink to the occasion and they would then at once be put to bed in the same room.

Construction methods were also similar to the canal age as instanced by the pioneer Harecastle tunnel on the Trent & Mersey. After trial borings a series of shafts, about 10ft [3m] in diameter, were sunk down to the level of the tunnel and it was then necessary to pump out what could be prodigious quantities of water. Once this was achieved, excavations would take place in opposite directions from the bottom of each shaft with the initial objective of creating a driftway, often no more than 4ft high by 3ft 6in wide [1.2 x 1.05m]. Connecting all the shafts and running the full length of the tunnel, it

The early stages of sinking a shaft by means of a horse-gin. Two horses are led round a circular gin-race to work the winding gear. Drawing by Les Turner. (YDNPA)

would hopefully confirm that all was well with initial surveying and alignment. Work would then start on enlarging the tunnel to its final dimensions, again excavating in two directions from the foot of the shaft with each heading having up to fifteen men working in the confined space.

The shafts acted as vital arteries for construction in taking men and materials – principally bricks and cement – down to the headings and bringing back waste spoil. Winding gear was increasingly steam powered but many shafts still had horse-gins as had long been the practice in coal and lead mines. A pair of gin boys would handle two horses going round a circular gin-race and keep a careful watch on the supply of oats, hay and straw.

Navvies divided into teams of top and bottom men. Those on the surface took tubs of brick on temporary tramways to the top of each shaft and returned with rock and clay to dump down a spoil bank. Mechanics, firemen and sundry craftsmen – known collectively as the 'black gang' – looked after the steam engines and winding gear.

Below ground, labourers toiling by candlelight in perpetual darkness wheeled

tubs of spoil into position for hoisting and brought bricks back to the headings. Here were skilled men, familiar with explosives but having no scruples about working with a lethal combination of matches, gunpowder and a clay pipe. Holes were hand-drilled in the rock face, filled with powder and tamped with clay. A primitive fuse, commonly no more than paper or straw, was then lit and the men hastened to what was considered a safe retreat. Unfortunately the distance was often misjudged resulting in fatalities and numerous injuries. A slow-burning fuse had been invented in the Cornish tin mines but was considered too expensive by most contractors and of no help to bonus-conscious miners who preferred to take the risk.

The resulting dust and sulphurous smoke could take well over an hour to clear and gave rise to deteriorating health conditions such as bronchitis and especially silicosis. The position got worse as tunnels lengthened and construction would last for several years with work continuing on a 24-hour basis six days a week. The only exception was normally Sunday with contractors facing a substantial fine if they broke the Sabbath.

Early railway tunnels pre-dated photography, but a good impression of working conditions is given in this later picture of lead miners. They are drilling into the rock in readiness for blasting. (Beamish Museum)

Landowners could sometimes insist on elaborate portals as happened at Bramhope, near Leeds. The larger tower had a spiral staircase leading to a belvedere from which the surrounding land could be viewed.

Pioneer tunnels often made a grand statement to symbolise the new railway age.
Opposite: A lone figure in the snow emphasises the monumental scale of Box tunnel's 40ft high portal on the Great Western Railway.
Right: Kilsby tunnel, near Rugby, completed in 1838 by Robert Stephenson.
(Wikimedia – 2)

KILSBY TUNNEL.

Trunk lines

Potential problems were highlighted by the first great trunk line out of London. Sanctioned by Parliament in 1833, the London & Birmingham Railway was engineered by Robert Stephenson and at Kilsby, south of Rugby, had the world's then longest railway tunnel at 1 mile 666yd (2.21km).

Within a few months of construction starting, the second working shaft was flooded owing to large amounts of quicksand not revealed by trial borings. The position became so severe that abandoning the shaft and restarting elsewhere was seriously considered. Several steam-powered pumps were installed to extract water at the rate of 2,000 gallons a minute, night and day, for eight months. Many abortive attempts were made to construct the brick lining by floating men and materials into position and stress is said to have caused the ill health and death of the contractor John Nowell. By the time the last brick was laid in June 1838, the tunnel had cost £320,000 [£29 million] – well over three times the original estimate – and 26 of

the 1,250 workers had died. It began a familiar pattern of both time and costs far exceeding expectations but was fully justified. Today it still forms an essential part of the West Coast Main Line.

The second trunk line out of London was in a different league, created by a man revered as one of the most innovative and prolific figures of the industrial revolution. Isambard Kingdom Brunel set new standards for building railways, designed ships that revolutionised naval engineering and bravely adopted the wider 7ft [2.14m] gauge of track for his magnificent Great Western Railway with its commanding tunnel at Box, between Bath and Chippenham.

He also worked with his father Marc Brunel on the earlier Thames Tunnel. Although designed for horse-drawn coaches and not initially used by trains, it was claimed to be the first to be successfully driven under a navigable river. Using a patented tunnelling shield, it took 18 years to complete and nearly caused the death of Isambard when the workings flooded. He had to be sent to Bristol

Tradition has always held that the engineering genius, Isambard Kingdom Brunel, aligned Box tunnel so that the rising sun shines through it on the date of his birthday – April 9th. Temporary closure for electrification work in April 2017 did not dispel this legend – and also produced some dramatic lighting. (Great Western Railway)

to recuperate and there heard about another project that was to set him on a path to glory – the unique Clifton Suspension Bridge.

Brunel began work on Box tunnel in December 1838 despite doubts that it would be impractical owing to unstable geological strata, its length of 1 mile 1,452yd [2.92km] and a width of 30ft (9.1m) to accommodate the broad-gauge tracks. The main contractor was George Burge, a well-established builder from Herne Bay, who with a mixture of confidence and optimism undertook to have the tunnel ready to hand over to the railway company within thirty months.

In a similar spirit of exuberance, Brunel recognised that the western portal would be in full view of the London to Bath road and designed it in a grand classical style as a celebratory monument to a new form of travel. It is still widely believed that he aligned the tunnel to enable the rising sun to be visible through it on his birthday – April 9th!

As at Kilsby, there were huge problems with water gushing into the workings and additional steam pumps were required. It was again a night-and-day operation, initially employing more than 1,500 men and over 100 horses. It seems scarcely credible that these numbers should later be almost trebled. Each week saw the use of a ton of candles and a ton of gunpowder, with carelessness in its use a contributory factor in a final death tally of almost a hundred men.

When work on Box tunnel began in 1838, it coincided with George Stephenson starting construction of the first railway to pierce the Pennines. With two of the greatest engineers of their day deeply committed to similar adventurous undertakings, there must have been more than curiosity over which would be the first to be completed. It was to prove close-run.

2

First Line through the Pennines

Summit Tunnel

Manchester Victoria station (A F Tait lithograph)

Manchester & Leeds Railway

Optimism prior to the 1825 opening of the Stockton & Darlington Railway led to many other proposed lines including one extending across England from Liverpool to Hull. It was strongly supported in Manchester, keen to repeat past success in the canal age less than 50 years earlier when it was linked by waterways to both ports. After much deliberation the project lapsed so that experience gained in constructing and operating the Liverpool & Manchester line could carefully be assessed. It again came to the fore when the first wave of railway promotion on a national scale gathered strength in the mid-1830s.

Manchester was continuing to expand prodigiously. Its growth and resulting evils were evocatively captured in 1835 by the French political thinker Alexis de Tocqueville: 'A thick black smoke covers the city. The sun appears like a disc without any rays. In this semi-daylight, 300,000 people work ceaselessly … The crunching wheels of machinery, the shriek of steam boilers, the regular beat of the looms, the heavy rumble of carts, those are the noises from which you can never escape in the sombre half-light of these streets.'

Such grim conditions did nothing to dent the desire for ever-more trade and railways heading east not just to Hull but also serving Leeds. Here the population was a much smaller 125,000 but it too was growing fast as befitted the largest settlement on the Yorkshire side of the Pennines.

Ambition began to turn into reality in 1836 when Parliament sanctioned three trunk lines of crucial importance. The Manchester & Leeds Railway followed the same obvious low-lying route as its steadfast opponents – the Rochdale Canal and the Calder & Hebble Navigation. On reaching Normanton, east of Wakefield, it was given powers to run into Leeds over the North Midland Railway, which at its southern end connected at Derby with lines from London and Birmingham. Normanton was also the junction with a third company, providing rail access to York and linking up with a line to Hull. The rail network was fast taking shape with Manchester playing a crucial part.

George Stephenson, the engineer for all three companies meeting at Normanton, was undertaking the last of his great works. As a disciple of minimum gradients on main-line railways, even at the expense of increased distance, he would not be troubled by the roundabout route from Manchester to Leeds extending to over 60 miles [96km] compared with little more than 40 miles in a straight line. As elsewhere, he mitigated the damage by avoiding detours to serve nearby towns and the only places of importance on the first main line through the Pennines were Rochdale and Wakefield.

Summit Tunnel

Walsden Gorge used by the Rochdale Canal gave Stephenson a dream ticket. It was not the first time he had seized on the results of Ice Age glaciation. Earlier in 1836 he had completed the Whitby & Pickering Railway, where the spectacular Newtondale Gorge today provides a highlight of the preserved North Yorkshire Moors line. A less determined engineer might have been tempted to favour the same approach as William Jessop had adopted for the canal and go straight over the top without a tunnel, but Stephenson would have none of it. He was adamant that there must be no lengthy gradients steeper than 1 in 150 on the climb out of Manchester and therefore a tunnel could not be avoided. A fortunate choice as his assistant engineer was Thomas Longridge Gooch, elder brother of

Daniel – the celebrated locomotive engineer and chairman of the Great Western Railway. Thomas spent his days out in the field looking at the best possible routes and then his nights plotting results and drawing plans.

The terminology of Summit tunnel has long confused geographers. With Walsden Gorge orientated south to north they see it as entirely logical that it should use the same points of the compass. Most railwaymen take a different view and insist that the tunnel has a west portal at its Manchester end and an east portal at the opposite end. To them it is on a main line running from west to east and the gorge is only an inconvenient hiccup in its overall direction.

There are further complications. Towards the top the railway is in a confined setting

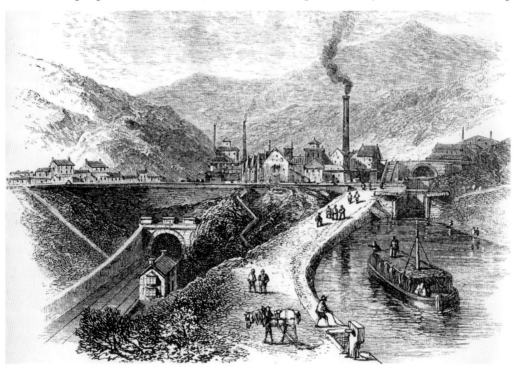

Arrangements at the Manchester end of the Summit tunnels are photographically a challenge, but were well captured by the Victorian artist Percival Skelton. His wood engraving may not be accurate in detail, but it shows how the Rochdale Canal rose through a series of locks to reach its highest point. Forced into a deep cutting in order to maintain an acceptable gradient, the railway is about to enter **Summit West tunnel.** (John Marshall collection – Kidderminster Railway Museum)

Summit Tunnel East signal box. The name indicates the ultimate direction of the line, even though it is heading south to north at this point.

The more spacious surroundings at the Yorkshire side of Summit. A very dirty 'Black 5' No. 44729 is heading a Liverpool to Leeds express in June 1961. (Gavin Morrison)

and only maintains its minimum gradient by means of a deep cutting with the canal at a much higher level. It enters the 55yd [48m] Summit West tunnel, which was bestowed with a crest combining the arms of Manchester and Leeds carved in the pediment. After passing under the turnpike road, it then briefly emerges into daylight before plunging through an imposing entrance into the main 1 mile 1,125yd [2.63km] Summit tunnel. At its opposite end a large oval shaft precedes the 41yd [37m] Summit East tunnel, where the more spacious surroundings proved less of an engineering challenge.

The crest heralding the start of this convoluted sequence was inscribed with the year 1839. It was certainly optimistic as regards completion of the line at Summit, but 4th July saw great crowds witnessing the first trains to run from Oldham Road terminus in Manchester through Rochdale to Littleborough. At the opposite end of the line, inauguration of services between Hebden Bridge and Normanton on 5th October 1840 fell far short of today's Health & Safety requirements. The carriages became so crowded that passengers resorted to standing on the roof and then ducking as they passed under the many bridges.

On the still incomplete section of line between Littleborough and Hebden Bridge, there were numerous delays at Summit tunnel where work had begun in January 1838 by sinking fourteen shafts on the bleak moorland to give access to the workings. The labour force varied between 750 and 1,250 men and boys aided by stationary steam engines. The tunnel lining required at least six courses of bricks, moved by over a hundred horses from a yard some three miles distant and using some 8,000 tons of cement brought by barge from Hull. Below ground, men were dependent on candlelight, hand tools and sheer physical strength. Work continued round the clock with miners and bricklayers

Plaque at Littleborough station commemorating both the initial opening and completion of the Manchester & Leeds Railway. (Lancashire & Yorkshire Railway Society)

receiving a maximum wage of 6s 6d [£30] for a ten-hour shift. It was an enormous sum when compared with the pittance earned by a common labourer, who was lucky to receive a quarter of this amount.

Accidents could scarcely be avoided and 41 lives were eventually lost. A letter to the *Railway Times* on behalf of the main contractor John Stephenson (no relation of George) explained that this was 'attributable to the carelessness or misconduct of the men themselves'. It added that a hospital had been erected and a surgeon was being paid £20 [£1,820] a month. Finally, it stated a preference for employing 'steady, sober, moral men rather than more experienced and better workmen who are drunken and dissolute'. Accordingly, £30 [£2,730] had been given towards erecting a place of worship to encourage temperance and spiritual welfare.

Summit tunnel cost £251,000 [£23 million] – a figure way in excess of the original estimate of £156,800 [£14.4 million]. It was nevertheless a great occasion on 9th

Although less than twenty miles from the centre of Manchester, the moors above Summit tunnel are surprisingly bleak. Shafts sunk for its building and retained for ventilation are a conspicuous landmark. (Tim Green of Bradford)

December 1840 when Barnard Dickinson, the engineer responsible for its construction, finally laid the last of its 23 million bricks. George Stephenson presented him with a silver trowel and in a moment of witticism asked that care be taken not to waste any cement!

The *Manchester Guardian* reflected the social niceties of the new Victorian age: 'Gentlemen of the first respectability accompanied by numbers of ladies were seen with lighted torches advancing towards the place to witness the ceremony of the completion of this great work. Subsequently the ladies and gentlemen present were invited to a cold collation at the Summit Inn.' The report ended succinctly by leaving no doubts on class distinction: 'The workmen were regaled in the tunnel.'

The most prophetic and telling comment of the day was made by Dickinson, who claimed

that the tunnel 'defies the rage of tempest, fire or war or wasting age'. As recounted in the closing pages of this book, these words struck home well over a century later when disaster occurred in the most spectacular style.

His work done, George Stephenson now resigned as the company's engineer. He was not a natural orator but was clearly more than satisfied with what he had achieved. Samuel Smiles, author of the Victorian best-seller *Self-Help*, quotes him as saying: 'I will stake my character and my head, if that tunnel ever give way, so as to cause danger to any of the public travelling through it. Taking it as a whole, I don't think there is such another piece of work in the world. It is the greatest work that has yet been done of its kind.'

Opening to passenger traffic of what proved to be the only double-track tunnel through the Pennine watershed for the next 53 years took place on 1st March 1841.

It meant that Summit had wrestled from Kilsby the distinction of being the longest railway tunnel in the world but it was not to last. Four months later on 30th June, work was completed at Box – only 327yd (296m) longer but it was enough. Brunel was ecstatic, especially on learning that the two ends were joined with an error of less than two inches (50mm) in their alignment. It was a great step forward compared with the canal age, when limitations in surveying meant that many tunnels had a pronounced kink in the middle. As a gesture of appreciation, he reputedly removed a ring from his finger and gave it to the works foreman.

Travel was changing fast, although prejudices had still to be overcome. At Box it was found that many passengers feared the subterranean journey and left the train at the preceding station. They then continued by road to the other end where they would wait for the following service. Although it was not put into effect, the Board of Trade favoured a scheme to overcome these fears: 'Lighting would add essentially to the comfort of travellers, and in some degree to their safety, for as it is not the practice of this railway to have white lights at the head of the engines, the drivers have at present no means of discovering any obstruction that there might be on the rails in front of them.'

Summit tunnel caused similar terrors, especially for travellers out of Manchester with engines working hard on the continuous climb. Early accounts refer to two torches being placed on the locomotive and tender in the hope that they 'afford some comfort to the passengers'.

The Tait lithographs

Just gazing down from the turnpike to the tunnel's commanding west portal far below was enough to cause acute palpitations among sensitive travellers. It was a spectacle ably captured by the accomplished artist Arthur Fitzwilliam Tait. Born near Liverpool in 1819, he was unable to make a living from the normal practice of drawing churches and so turned his attention to producing lithographs of railway subjects. The exciting new mode of transport meant these were in great demand in an age prior to photography. Twenty such illustrations were collected together in his superb *Views on the Manchester and Leeds Railway*, which would be treasured by those with the required cash and sufficient shelf space in their library to accommodate its generous dimensions.

The lithograph of Summit tunnel sets the tone by giving an accurate impression of challenges to be overcome in building the line. Few artists would have resisted the temptation to exaggerate the scale of the triangular mound rising immediately behind the tunnel mouth, but present-day photographs show that the finished result had an acceptable degree of restraint. Accompanying text by Edwin Butterworth suitably captured the thrall of passing through the tunnel:

'The rapidity of the flight, the screech of the warning signal from the engine, the overhanging column of mingled smoke and steam, the rush of air, together with the lurid glare and innumerable sparks thrown by the flambeaux which the train carries, and others borne by persons stationed in the tunnel, conspire, with feeling that we are passing through the body of a huge mountain, to excite and awe our mind; for there we are,

The drama of the Manchester end of Summit tunnel superbly captured by A F Tait. It shows in detail the imposing design of the portal that was deliberately over-sized for maximum effect.

Below right: Tait avoided extreme artistic licence, although he did give the impression that there was a rocky peak above Summit tunnel entrance. It is in fact spoil dumped when the excavations were in progress. (Flickr – Ingy the Wingy)

WEST ENTRANCE SUMMIT TUNNEL.

if out of peril, yet, in the very midst of the stupendous works of nature, and the highest triumphs of human enterprise.'

Other lithographs convey the difficulty of fitting the railway into the narrow valley between Summit and Hebden Bridge that was already uncomfortably full with its canal, river and road. Where the canal had to be crossed, as happened at Gauxholme near Todmorden, a skew bridge had to be built on an acute angle. Edwin Butterworth described it as 'a costly and beautiful structure … supported at the angles by handsome castellated abutments of solid masonry, and yet possessing a most graceful appearance'. Photographs of recent times emphasise what was achieved in such a constricted setting.

Several of the Tait lithographs have at various times been published in tinted versions. His study of Gauxholme viaduct, near Todmorden, shows the 102ft cast-iron span boldly striding across the Rochdale Canal.

Much development has taken place since Tait's time but Gauxholme viaduct still dominates the scene. Strengthening in 1906 by steel girders is clearly visible in this view of a Scarborough to Holyhead service in August 1984. (Gavin Morrison)

WHITELEYS VIADUCT CHARLESTON CLOUGH

Whiteley's viaduct, west of Hebden Bridge, with much activity on earlier forms of transport represented by turnpike road and canal.

Similarly, a lithograph of Whiteley's viaduct west of Hebden Bridge shows how the railway was unable to follow the valley floor and had to run on a shelf cut into the hillside. With traffic on the turnpike, a barge on the canal and a distant train, it is only too evident that three modes of transport were forced to vie for space. The viaduct, which took its name from the owners of nearby Calderside Mill, was similar to Gauxholme in making innovative use of cast-iron bowstring girders for its main span.

The building on the left of the train was probably a pump house for watering locomotives and would be connected to the tall chimney realistically included in the picture. Just beyond this point at Charlestown, work on providing a short tunnel had to be abandoned when the excavations constantly collapsed. It was replaced by what was intended to be a temporary and sharply curved deviation but instead became permanent. The curves were finally re-aligned when the 1912 derailment of an express with the loss of four lives was attributed to excessive speed.

Tait also illustrated some of the stations. At Rochdale he gives prominence to the main buildings, parts of which survived until the 1970s. In the distance he shows the engine shed with its pump-house chimney and a locomotive standing next to the water

The S-shaped Charlestown curve in the narrowest part of the Calder valley was created when an intended tunnel collapsed. A Burnley to Scarborough train is proceeding at a suitable pace in April 1978. (Gavin Morrison)

Right: Charlestown curve was realigned after its sharpness was a factor in this disastrous derailment of a Manchester to Leeds express on 21st June 1912.

Rochdale station. The text accompanying the Tait lithographs comments that it is 'a small but yet commodious and neat edifice'.

The main station buildings, left of centre in the Tait lithograph, had lost their awning but were still in use as the district engineer's office in the 1970s. (J B Hodgson)

crane. The most 'active' of all his lithographs depicts 'Brighouse for Bradford', the suffix indicating that this was where passengers left the train for an uncomfortable seven-mile [11.3km] journey over hill roads. It includes a platelayer's trolley with three men directing operations alongside the low-level platform and a patient shunting horse ready to move a flat truck loaded with rails.

The two-storey station is impressive in size and in some quarters the company's buildings were considered to be extravagant. It was a view taken by the civil engineer Francis Whishaw in his monumental tome *The Railways of Great Britain and Ireland,* first published in 1840. In a work with its unusual dedication to 'The Railway Capitalists of the United Kingdom', it is perhaps not surprising that he felt adopting a simpler style of architecture and 'avoiding the erection of so many Elizabethan buildings' would have saved expense.

Finally, Tait turned his attention to Normanton as an important meeting point of three separate companies. He shows the two island platforms with the civilised arrangement of a covered footbridge linking them to the station hotel and refreshment rooms. Normanton later became famous for providing passengers with a five-course meal when expresses made a half-hour pause, but the advent of restaurant cars put an end to the days of gobbling food and serious indigestion. E L Ahrons, one of the most acerbic railway writers of the time, lamented that it became 'a sight something of the nature of the Sahara desert furnished with a beer pump'.

Tinted version of the Tait lithograph of Brighouse station. The building on the far left could be a pump house for the water crane on the extreme right.

The lithograph of Normanton provides an invaluable record of this important early railway junction in the era before photography. Built jointly by all three companies using the station, it included the then rare feature of a covered footbridge leading to the hotel.

The rebuilt Normanton station was acquiring a ghostly air of neglect when seen here in 1975, but the covered footbridge remained a remarkable survival.

Changing times

Normanton in its heyday was one of the busiest of railway junctions, as lines from Derby to Leeds as well as onto York and Hull had all been opened in 1840. By day it became notorious for its surly and unhelpful porters, with one correspondent to the *Railway Times* complaining that it was 'quite unfit for any respectable female to attempt to stop at Normanton if she has any luggage with her'. At night it handled vast quantities of mail traffic. Instead of running through to Leeds, the last train of the day from Manchester at 10.0pm terminated there at 12.25am for sacks of post and parcels to be duly unloaded. A return mail service left at 6.0am.

This was reflected in the company's first 1841 timetable, an impressive document giving far more than just the times of the ten weekday trains each way. It included details of where they would be met by 'stage coaches and omnibuses' and gave a useful summary of rules and regulations. Way ahead of a future change in attitude was a prohibition of smoking on any railway premises and there was one statement remarkable for its all-embracing choice of words: 'The company do not hold themselves responsible for any luggage, matter, or thing, unless booked, and paid for accordingly.'

Yet despite hope that all would be well received, there were two areas that caused serious dispute. The first was a decision to run Sunday trains, which led to the resignation of the chairman and two directors. Even though the Lord's Day Observance Society had recently been formed and opposition was vehement, the company refused to back down. It was serving a large working-class population and took the view that it was providing Sunday solace as an escape from six days of mill life. The *Manchester Guardian* may have been over the top in enthusiastically celebrating the great numbers 'enjoying the pure air in the mountainous neighbourhood of Rochdale', but there was no going back on a public demand for Sunday travel.

More difficult to resolve were issues arising from a single sentence in the timetable: 'Every train will have First and Second Class carriages, and some of them, for the convenience of the Working Classes, open wagons without seats.' It was the last four words that caused the real problems. Wagon Class, as it was sometimes termed, was definitely a shocking 3rd Class and conditions in the wild Pennines could be grim in the extreme. The railway historian Thomas Normington recalled one such journey in the 1840s:

'The carriage was simply a square wood box or wagon without seats or roof, exposed to all sorts of weather and the passengers all wedged in like cattle in a truck. I was in my Sunday clothes and had on a new top hat. To my surprise and sorrow on emerging out of Summit tunnel I found my new hat entirely spoilt, the down having been frizzled up by the small hot cinders emitted from the funnel of the engine.'

There may have been an element of low comedy but local papers were not amused. The *Halifax Courier* reported that passengers were being forced to share open wagons with livestock and there was icy condemnation in the *Leeds Intelligencer*: 'They must put seats in their third class carriages and not stow human beings away in them like so many pigs and sheep.'

Making matters worse was company policy that its porters were not allowed to carry the luggage of wagon passengers, who were also restricted as to the trains they could use. A timetable note laconically stated that the first 6.45am departure from Manchester was the only service on which it was possible to go through to London by wagon. The thought of such a journey, potentially standing for many hours in wind and rain with changes at

Contrasts in Manchester & Leeds Railway carriages. At top is a composite with no protection from the weather for 2nd Class passengers. The more luxurious carriage in the lower illustration is solely 1st Class and included provision for guards to travel on the roof. (Rixon Bucknall collection)

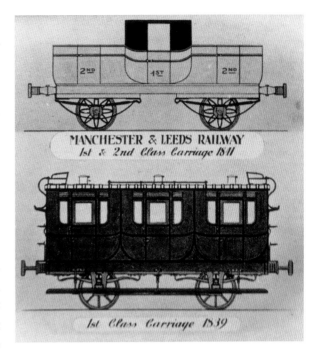

MANCHESTER & LEEDS RAILWAY
1st & 2nd Class Carriage 1841

1st Class Carriage 1839

Normanton and Rugby, seems too awful to contemplate.

Not helping was the contrast with carriages for the more well-to-do. There was initially a half-way stage with a composite vehicle that had a covered 1st Class centre compartment with 2nd Class at either end providing ample fresh air. Carriages catering solely for 1st Class passengers were definitely of a higher order, although there were some curious reminders of former times. Seats were provided on the roof for guards, dressed in flaming red, who often carried horns as if they were on a stagecoach. The running board at wheel level was partly to help passengers get in and out of their compartments but was also bravely used by ticket collectors when the train was in motion.

The opulence of a 1st Class carriage received high praise in a March 1841 issue of the *Railway Times*: 'The interior of this compartment is fitted up to give the appearance of a splendid saloon with rich carved mahogany sofas lined with crimson plush and trimmed with silk gimp, and at each corner is a mirror of large dimensions. The painting is of very superior character, the body being of a handsome lemon colour; and above the panels are emblazoned the arms of Manchester, Leeds, London, York, Hull, Birmingham and Derby, painted in most beautiful relief to the rich and delicate body colour.'

Should this not provide sufficient exclusiveness, there were arrangements for gentlemen to put a coach on a special carriage truck provided with drop-down ends as an early forerunner of roll-on/roll-off facilities. They could then remain cocooned in the comfort of their own coach for the journey. It was characteristic of an age so divided by gender and class that the timetable makes no mention of their ladies but does refer to 'servants riding outside, and children, wagon fare'.

One consequence was the many different rates of travel, which cynics would say was destined to endure to the present day. Relatively straightforward was 1st Class at 3d [£1.20] per mile, with 2nd Class at 2d and the railway equivalent of steerage generally costing 1d. It was the willingness to carry livestock in the same trains as passengers that greatly added to the complications. There were many different rates ranging from horses and oxen down to calves and pigs.

It was perhaps fortunate that the chief booking-clerk at Manchester was Thomas

Edmondson, noted as the inventor of a machine for dating and progressively numbering printed railway tickets. The company was able to claim that on a single day it prevented 110 attempts at fraud. A homely touch was provided by tickets for travel towards Leeds having a fleece engraved on the back and those for the reverse direction featuring a bale of cotton.

Book-keeping could be tedious in the extreme and rarely merited public notice. Hence there is a certain irony that neglect by a junior clerk should be sufficient to put him second only to George Stephenson among those indelibly associated with the Manchester & Leeds Railway. His name was Branwell Brontë.

At the age of 23 he left the company of his three literary sisters at Haworth Parsonage and in August 1840 obtained the post of assistant clerk-in-charge at the newly opened Sowerby Bridge station. Eight months later he was promoted to similar work at Luddendenfoot on an improved salary of £130 [£11,900] a year. There he struck up a friendship with a young railway engineer, Francis Grundy, who penned a bleak picture of him working in a 'rude wooden hut' and going 'thoroughly to the bad'.

Deprived of any stimulating company, Branwell left a porter in charge and went drinking in local pubs. His undoing came when an audit of the station ledgers revealed a discrepancy of a little over £11 [£1,000]. The amount was deducted from his salary and according to Grundy he was 'convicted of constant and culpable carelessness'. Dismissal took effect in March 1842 and Branwell lived for only another six years before dying a broken man due to tuberculosis with the end hastened by drink and opium.

Luddendenfoot station, midway between Mytholmroyd and Sowerby Bridge, closed in 1962 and is today best remembered for the misdoings of its assistant clerk Branwell Brontë. In busier times it had a staff of six, most of them smartly attired with collar and tie. (Stuart Rankin collection)

Cautious expansion

By the early 1840s the Manchester & Leeds Railway had more important issues on its mind than the evils of Sunday trains, condemnation through putting passengers in open wagons as if they were pigs, or the wrongdoings of a station clerk. The wave of optimism responsible for its creation in 1836 had been followed by prolonged depression culminating in a general strike with mills shut down and armed militia firing at rioters. The company was nevertheless about to realise an ambition cherished since its earliest days.

After much delay, its services were transferred to a new station in the centre of Manchester, named Victoria after the young queen and opened on 1st January 1844. Although then the largest station in Britain, it had just one platform 850ft [255m] in length. Four months later, it also began to be used by trains coming in from the west on the pioneer Liverpool & Manchester Railway. Lack of joint management constantly foiled hopes of easy transfer from one end of the platform to the other, but it was undoubtedly a pivotal moment. Through rail travel was now possible between Liverpool and Hull – it was the equivalent of completion of the M62.

In a renewed spirit of cautious optimism, the Manchester & Leeds had already embarked on gradual expansion to protect its position with a series of offshoots from its main line. Close to Manchester was a 6½-mile branch from Miles Platting to the Tame valley town of Stalybridge, surveyed in 1843 by Thomas Gooch at the same time as many other lines. The 'railway mania' with numerous abortive ventures was in sight and it proved too much for him. In twenty years of strenuous work, including the supreme challenge of Summit tunnel, his only holiday had been three days' honeymoon. He was forced to resign on health grounds and was succeeded as the company's chief civil engineer by John Hawkshaw, whose salary of £5,000 [£500,000] was later cut by half at a stormy board meeting.

The Stalybridge branch proved to be baptism by fire for Hawkshaw, largely due to problems with boggy land that swiftly turned into oozing quagmire. Horses floundered on planks and the trackbed had to be excavated to a depth of some five feet before brushwood, clay and ballast were added. Opening was delayed until 5th October 1846.

Although only a little further north, conditions could scarcely have been more

Werneth, the original 1842 terminus of the Oldham branch, had a sparse interior remarkably similar at the time to that of a chapel.
(J B Hodgson)

Opening of Werneth tunnel, Oldham, in 1847 coincided with the creation of the Lancashire & Yorkshire Railway, which therefore had its crest above the west portal. (J B Hodgson)

different at Oldham – one of the towns swept to one side by George Stephenson when planning his main line through the Pennines with the easiest possible gradients. A totally opposite approach resulted in a two-mile connecting branch terminating at Werneth on the western edge of the town after climbing a gradient of 1 in 27 – one of the steepest in the country to be used by passenger services. It was too demanding an incline for early locomotives and trains were initially attached to a wire rope passing round a drum at the summit. A descending train then counterbalanced the operation.

Sanctioned in 1839 and opened on 31st March 1842, it took another five years for the branch to be extended through a 471yd [429m] tunnel to a station in the town centre with the curious name of Mumps. It was at its busiest when the mills shut in south Lancashire towns such as Oldham for the traditional Whitsun Wakes Week. Shortly

after opening, the company decided to issue Blackpool-bound excursionists with tickets priced at 1s 6d [£7.10] for gentlemen and 1s 0d [£4.70] for ladies. Thomas Normington, then the stationmaster at Mumps, relates how men were suspected of masquerading as women to get the cheaper fare. Matters came to a head when a superintendent called in to investigate was knocked to the ground by angry passengers and had to be dragged unconscious into a waiting room.

No such excitement affected the 1¾-mile branch from the main line at Blue Pits, south of Rochdale, to Heywood. Opening on 15th April 1841, traffic was so modest that trains were horse-hauled for the first six years.

A more ambitious venture was a nine-mile route authorised in 1845 to connect the main line at Todmorden with Burnley. Using Cliviger Gorge, another glacial meltwater channel close to Walsden Gorge, it similarly provided one of the few low-level passes

One consequence of steep gradients on the Todmorden-Burnley line was that heavy coal trains required banking to Copy Pit summit. Three months before the end of steam on British Railways, one such train is starting the three-mile climb on 18th May 1968 headed by 8F No. 48410. Sister locomotive No. 48519 is in the distance waiting to give rear-end assistance. (Gavin Morrison)

Once at Copy Pit summit, No. 48519 drops off and the train continues towards Burnley. (Gavin Morrison)

Nott Wood viaduct, less than two miles west of Todmorden, is crossed in October 1980 by a special making a lengthy journey from Shoeburyness to Blackpool. (Gavin Morrison)

through the Pennine watershed but still reached the 750ft [230m] contour. Had it been conceived a decade earlier with George Stephenson as its engineer, it could well have fallen into the exclusive group of railways piercing the mountain chain by means of a long tunnel.

Instead, the improving capability of locomotives was now recognised and there were gradients steeper than 1 in 70 either side of a tunnel-free Copy Pit summit. It was a substantially cheaper construction but meant that long trains from the Yorkshire coalfields had to be banked out of Todmorden. Opened on 12th November 1849, it provided passengers heading to Preston and Blackpool with an attractive stretch of railway including an impressive Nott Wood viaduct at Lydgate.

The further the main line headed deeper into Yorkshire from the centre of power in Manchester, so did accusations of neglect increase. This was certainly the case in Halifax, which like Oldham was another

of the towns bypassed by Stephenson. Hopes were not high, even when Parliament specified in 1839 that a 1¾-mile branch from a junction with the main line near Greetland should be constructed 'as speedily as possible' and completed within three years. It seemed an all too familiar pattern of events when nothing had happened at the end of this period. Halifax was still smarting from having to wait until the virtual end of the canal age in 1828 for completion of a branch of the Calder & Hebble Navigation into the centre of the town.

Not until 1843 were plans finally prepared and the single-track branch opened to a temporary terminus on 1st July 1844. There was still seething resentment owing to poor connections with main-line services, while the 1 in 44 gradient meant that many trains stalled on the bank and had to set back for a second run. Cotton manufacture was now eroding the local monopoly of wool and working conditions were fast deteriorating

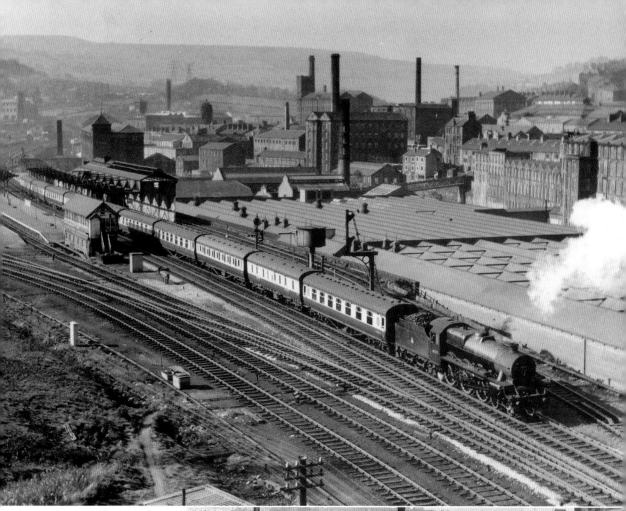

The changing face of Sowerby Bridge – one of the junctions for services to Halifax and Bradford. These two matchless black-and-white pictures by the famous photographer Bishop Eric Treacy show the railway at its maximum extent. In one of them, 'Jubilee' No. 45717 *Dauntless* is heading a Liverpool to York express, and both have mill chimneys everywhere.

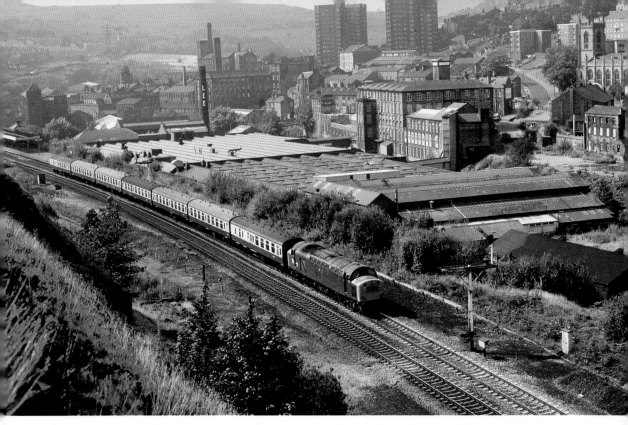

Sowerby Bridge in 1976, when much of the trackwork and most of the chimneys had gone. A summer Saturday service from Blackpool is heading towards Bradford. (Gavin Morrison)

with ever-increasing numbers of mills reducing average life expectancy to a mere 26 years. Charles Dickens endured over two hours in Halifax to give one of his famous readings, but afterwards wrote: 'It is as horrible a place as I ever saw.'

In 1852 a more realistically graded connection was opened from Sowerby Bridge and the temporary station was replaced when the line was extended to Bradford. In rejoicing at the passing of the 'miserable, dirty and disagreeable' facilities, the *Halifax Courier* commented: 'We are sure there is not a town from Caithness to Cornwall which could exhibit a more filthy doghole of a place than that in which all the railway traffic of Halifax has so long been conducted.'

Facilities at Bradford were no great improvement and gave ample ammunition for the pen of E L Ahrons, who wrote off the terminus as a dreadful bottleneck providing

'an unceasing wellspring of torrid language in which the railwaymen and the general public took a hearty share'. The root problem was an approach tunnel on a 1 in 50 gradient 'full of dense smoke, sulphur dioxide, and various compounds of tri-nitro profanity so that it was impossible to see two yards'.

There were great hopes of continuing into Leeds but these were never realised. Just as had happened at Normanton, it was necessary to rely on the lines of another company to enter the West Riding's most important settlement. Yet outwardly the Manchester & Leeds was expanding well beyond the area suggested by its title and on 9th July 1847 became the Lancashire & Yorkshire Railway. This may have reflected determined optimism but such was impoverishment and penny-pinching after the 'mania' collapse that for many years there was little chance of living up to higher ambition.

It gave further fuel for the evocative prose of Ahrons, who referred to 'a railway of ugly inconvenient stations, of old broken-down engines and dirty carriages, and of a superlative unpunctuality, to which no pen could do justice'. This did not stop condemnation of 'probably the most degenerate railway' in Britain. Its new title scarcely hid the fact that it was still a Lancashire-orientated company controlled from Manchester and thus seen as beyond hope from a Yorkshire perspective. The only redeeming feature was that its failings provided a rare source of agreement for inhabitants of the two counties, who otherwise argued over virtually everything from Yorkshire Pudding versus Lancashire Hotpot down to the finer points of county cricket.

Even in the late 1860s the company was still using cattle trucks on its excursion trains and imploring more respectable railways not to pamper 3rd Class travellers with foot-warmers. Yet at a higher level there was great concern when it learnt that 1st Class smoking compartments on a rival railway were provided with 'much superior' spittoons!

It also managed to indulge in wild flights of fancy as happened with an extraordinary scheme to forge the longest of all Pennine tunnels.

The tunnel that never was

In the mid-Victorian boom economy lasting into the 1870s, the Lancashire & Yorkshire decided to eliminate the kink in its main line that had existed ever since its inception by George Stephenson. It was seen as an alternative to going round almost three sides of a square via Walsden Gorge and the upper Calder Valley.

Working from the Yorkshire end, a more direct route was surveyed from the existing main line at Sowerby Bridge to climb up the Ryburn Valley through Ripponden and Rishworth. Passing the evocatively named Slithero Bottom, it entered a tunnel no less than four miles in length under Blackstone Edge, following a course very similar to that today taken at a much higher level by the M62. Emerging close to Hollingworth Lake, it rejoined the existing line south of Littleborough.

The grand plan for a shortened main line tunnelling under Blackstone Edge required replacement of the original station at Sowerby Bridge, which was badly sited for the new junction. This early photograph, reputedly taken in 1856, shows it prior to closure twenty years later.

A quarter mile to the east, the new 1876 station at Sowerby Bridge still had a strong emphasis on castellated turrets. (Stuart Rankin collection)

With determined optimism, a first positive step was made at Sowerby Bridge where the station was re-sited so that it could serve both the existing and proposed new lines. The replacement, noted for its impressive buildings, was opened on 1st September 1876. Work on a double-track main line up the Ryburn Valley was already in progress, but it may have been a bad omen that all was far from well.

The valley was narrower and even more steep-sided than that of the Calder below Todmorden. There were immense difficulties with a short 593yd [540m] tunnel on leaving Sowerby Bridge as well as constant problems with unstable land. The contract price for the first 3¾ miles through Ripponden to the small village of Rishworth had been £113,000 [£10 million] but by late 1876 total expenditure was a fraction under £200,000 [£19 million] and estimates for further required work totalled a startling £167,000 [£15.8 million]. These seem extraordinarily high amounts.

The board received a report that 'bar no further disaster' this section of line should be completed by the following summer but it was 5th August 1878 before the first passenger train pulled into Ripponden station. In reporting the celebrations with church bells ringing and a large cannon firing, the *Halifax Courier* concluded: 'It is expected that the company will continue the line under Blackstone Edge to Littleborough.'

Hopes must have been evaporating when well over two years elapsed before a short extension of less than a mile to Rishworth was opened on 1st March 1881. Its single platform, linked to the village by a lofty timber viaduct, seemed symbolic of changing fortunes. In the faltering Victorian economy it was not the time for continuing massive expenditure and the grand plan came to a halt. It was never resumed. All that remained was an incongruous twin-track branch built to main-line standards and destined to be a liability until the end of its existence. Its last passenger train ran in 1929.

Looking back, it is difficult to see why the great tunnel was ever seriously contemplated. It would have shortened the existing line by some five miles but would have involved 1 in 60 approach gradients and hence a minimal reduction in journey time. Quite what George Stephenson would have made of such a scheme can only be left to the imagination.

The proposed main line that became a mere branch, less than four miles in length, epitomised at Ripponden station in 1953. The double-track was still in place for goods traffic, which lasted for only another five years.

End of the line. Rishworth station was intended to precede a four-mile tunnel through to Littleborough, but instead became a terminus serving the tiniest of villages. Railway staff far outnumbering passengers became a regular occurrence prior to services ceasing as early as 1929.

The Lancashire & Yorkshire Railway eventually recovered from decadent years and became an efficient line with smart-looking expresses. Atlantic No. 1424 is near Mytholmroyd heading a dining car service from York to Manchester. (J B Hodgson collection)

Through to the present day

Only gradually did the Lancashire & Yorkshire change its ways, as neatly summed up in a single sentence by one of the most readable of railway authors Cuthbert Hamilton Ellis: 'It passed, by stages, through an extraordinary sequence of pride, decadence, ruinousness and renaissance, to become one of the most efficient railways in the kingdom.'

The company amalgamated with the London & North Western Railway on 1st January 1922, a year ahead of the 1923 Grouping when the combined concern became part of the LMS. There was remarkably little change to the Calder Valley main line until 1970 when through services along its entire length, generally from Newcastle to Liverpool, were withdrawn. With the increase in rail travel its western end now carries far more frequent trains than was previously the case, most of them travelling from Leeds via Bradford and Halifax to Manchester Victoria.

Here the station, once regularly voted 'Britain's worst' and seen as symbolic of depressed post-industrial Lancashire, is gradually being transformed as the figurehead of the 'Northern Powerhouse'. Work on a £44 million renovation scheme started in 2010, although there was an element of despair when a poster stated: 'Please bear with us while we make Victoria posh.' It now has a dramatic concourse with impressive arches and an overhead walkway.

The greatest change to frequency of services has been on the line to Burnley over Copy Pit summit, which came close to closure in 1965 but now carries Leeds to Preston and Blackpool trains running at hourly intervals. From 2015 these were augmented by workings from Manchester to Burnley passing through Summit tunnel and serving Todmorden. The first line through the Pennines is in good shape, 180 years since it was opened.

3

Twin Hell-Holes

Woodhead Tunnels

Miners drilling holes underground (Beamish Museum)

Sheffield to Manchester

The dismay evident in Oldham and Halifax when bypassed by the Manchester & Leeds Railway was on a minor scale when compared with a much larger town that was similarly cast aside by George Stephenson. At the 1831 census it had a population of 84,596, more than five times the 15,382 of Halifax, and was second only to Leeds as the largest settlement in the West Riding. That town was Sheffield.

Instead of cloth-making the industry responsible for its growth was cutlery. Chaucer's miller referred to 'a Sheffield thwitel' (a table knife) and by the 15th century there were numerous water grinding mills along the banks of its small rivers flowing down from the Peak District of Derbyshire. Steel making was established by 1780, but the town became increasingly handicapped by high hills forming a barrier to the south and west.

When Stephenson was appointed engineer of the North Midland Railway, he was adamant that its prime purpose was to link Derby with Leeds. He successfully argued that minimum gradients could only be achieved north of Chesterfield by a direct route along the Rother Valley. A deviation through the Drone and Sheaf Valleys to serve Sheffield would be circuitous, too steeply graded for the locomotives of the day and too costly. He got his way when the North Midland was incorporated in 1836 – the same year as the Manchester & Leeds.

It was not the first time that Sheffield was left with acute disappointment. There were parallels with Halifax in that there was no canal into the town centre until the relatively late date of 1819. Previously it was dependent on the Don Navigation, completed in 1751 and extending from its outskirts at Tinsley to Goole and the Humber estuary. Manchester was only 35 miles [56km] distant in a straight line but the Pennine chain was here at its most formidable. Plans in the 1820s for a Grand Commercial Canal linking South Yorkshire with Lancashire collapsed, yet all the while Sheffield was losing out due to increasing European competition in the American market for edge tools and cutlery. An average journey by inland waterways to Manchester took a week.

There was real hope in 1831 with a proposed Sheffield to Manchester railway. It was a most ambitious scheme for so early a date, ascending the Sheaf Valley by means of a 1 in 32 self-acting incline, plunging through a direct three-mile tunnel into the Hope valley, and then conquering the main barrier of Rushup Edge with the aid of four inclined planes. The engineers were George and Robert Stephenson, and doubts have been cast as to why leading advocates of locomotive haulage should put forward a scheme relying on rope working. One theory is that pressure of work drove them to take the unethical step of simply putting their names to the survey.

Optimism reached new heights on 23rd August 1831 when the Sheffield & Manchester Railway became the first line piercing the Pennines to be sanctioned by Parliament. It was only a year after opening of the Liverpool & Manchester and it looked as if Sheffield would now forge ahead of Leeds, which had no proposals for a rail link with Lancashire at such an advanced stage. There was one problem. Hamstrung by engineering obstacles and controversy over capital estimates, it was never built. By 1833 it was no more than a brave venture that faded away.

The need for a railway between the two centres was steadily increasing, as the remarkable pace of industrial expansion in Manchester and much of Lancashire meant that a good market for South Yorkshire coal was assured. It was now firmly into the period when a core railway network was fast taking shape and 1836 brought fresh proposals. It seemed that hopes long held in Sheffield would at last be realised. The turmoil, bitterness, divisive argument, human misery and sheer ordeal that lay ahead could not be imagined.

Troubled times

Potential problems should have been apparent from the outset. The difficulties that had plagued the Leeds & Liverpool Canal, with its separate committees in Yorkshire and Lancashire, were now firmly in the past, but it proved unfortunate that the same approach was initially taken. A cumbersome arrangement saw directors at each end of the line forming separate management committees in Sheffield and Manchester, each to approve the other's decisions before they were implemented. Attempting to maintain order was the chairman Lord Wharncliffe, a Yorkshire peer and a former Lord Privy Seal. The noted diarist Charles Greville described him as 'a spiritual, sensible, zealous, honourable, consistent country gentleman', but at times his patience must have been severely strained.

There was little difficulty in agreeing a route from Sheffield that would pass close to his seat at Wortley Hall, near Stocksbridge, and climb up the Don valley through Penistone to the treeless Pennine watershed. For an eagle-eyed bird of prey this was within sight of the head of Longdendale, which provided a direct descent from bleak moors with scarcely a sign of human habitation down to low-lying land close to Manchester.

Serious protests arose in Glossop, a new town recently created by squire Bernard Howard when he inherited the Dukedom of Norfolk. It was little more than a mile from the proposed route but this was not considered acceptable. Especially unhappy were several mill owners, all from the same family with the true northern surname of Sidebottom. It did not look promising when five of them were on the railway's Manchester committee, but common sense eventually had to prevail. Glossop was in such a bowl of surrounding hills that a vicious dog's leg would have been needed to bring the line closer to the town centre. The compromise was a connecting branch, privately built by one of the richest dukes in England and not requiring parliamentary sanction as he owned all the land. It had a sculptured lion, representing his family coat of arms, above the station entrance.

This issue resolved, attention could now turn to the more fundamental problem of how to cross the Pennine watershed. Another serious mistake may have been made when separate proposals were commissioned from two rival engineers. Charles Vignoles, born in Ireland in 1793, was a military man whose impetuous enthusiasm and fiery nature was prone to outweigh his judgment. He favoured accepting steep gradients and a summit level in excess of 1,000ft [300m] in order to limit the length of a tunnel to two miles.

Joseph Locke, a Sheffield man by birth, was twelve years younger but already held in high regard as an engineer noted for his cool and unruffled planning. He advocated a three-mile tunnel to keep gradients no steeper than 1 in 120 with a summit of 943ft [283m]. Lord Wharncliffe and George Sidebottom now had the demanding role of acting as peacemakers. The longer option was agreed but Vignoles was chosen as the company's engineer. It was an appointment that came to be deeply regretted.

Destined to have a dark reputation for more than a century, the 3 miles 22yd [4.82km] Woodhead tunnel posed challenges not hitherto contemplated in the railway age. It was a good mile longer than Box, which also had all the advantages of a low-lying location in southern England. The only tunnel of comparable length pre-dated railways but was close at hand at Standedge on the Huddersfield Canal. Its completion in 1811 was still within living memory and its many delays and enormous cost ought to have sounded an awful warning. Significantly, there was no encouragement from George Stephenson when he learnt what was intended. In characteristically gruff style, he remarked that he would eat the first locomotive to pass through the tunnel!

It may already have been considered a lost cause, as there was little opposition in Parliament to the 41-mile [66km] line. The Sheffield, Ashton-under-Lyne & Manchester Railway, taking is middle name from support received in the ancient market town on the

Joseph Locke, generally regarded as one of 'the great triumvirate' of railway engineers along with Isambard Kingdom Brunel and Robert Stephenson. He proposed a three-mile Woodhead tunnel as early as 1836.

edge of Cheshire, was sanctioned on 5th May 1837. County rivalry was still continuing and it may not have helped when the company's coat of arms was crowned with the Yorkshire white rose. Tensions were clearly evident when Thomas Ward resigned as the first secretary and clerk. He was a Sheffield man and could not abide a decision to site the head office in Manchester.

More difficult economic times were now prevailing and another decision destined to incur massive future costs was to limit the tunnel to single-track width. Acute shortage of funds meant it was October 1838 before Lord Wharncliffe and Vignoles cut the ceremonial first sod at Woodhead. Marquees were put up for guests and flags marked the route down the valley for many miles. Unusually for this part of the Pennines the weather was fine and clear, which may have given a false impression of conditions in the depths of winter. Vignoles optimistically ordered thirteen tents to shelter navvies working on the tunnel and urged a need for more permanent housing as well as shops and access roads.

Yet nothing was done and in that first winter some 400 men had to fend for themselves, bivouacked in huts thrown together with loose stones and thatched with ling from the moors. At night they slept in groups of twenty on truckle beds. It was not until May 1839 that contracts were let for providing better accommodation and over four miles of cart roads to bring in coal and building materials. By the time this work was complete it was September and relations between the company and Vignoles were becoming increasingly strained.

Construction had scarcely started and by comparison the Manchester & Leeds Railway had now opened its first 14 miles [22.5km] to Littleborough.

Exactly what happened next will never be entirely clear. It appears that Vignoles bought large numbers of shares in the company on a dubious basis and then found himself in financial difficulties. As a result he patched up a gentleman's agreement with Lord Wharncliffe to ease his liabilities but this proved unacceptable to the directors. Although the company minutes draw a veil over the scale of duplicity, it was clearly serious. By mid-1840 both Vignoles and the chairman had resigned.

Better progress

Appointing a new engineer was urgent and the company was fortunate that it could go back to square one and engage the services of Joseph Locke. Fresh from achievements on the Grand Junction and London & Southampton railways, he was able to set his own terms. He was given full responsibility for execution of the works, the right to select the resident or sub-engineers, and was expected to devote up to two months of his time during the year to the company. His annual salary was to be £750 [£68,000], increased to £1,000 [£91,000] when the western half of the line was completed. Locke had similar contracts with other railways, which suggests that an engineer of his standing had the potential to receive a comfortable half a million pounds per year in terms of modern money.

Better progress was achieved with strong Yorkshire influence maintained by the new chairman John Parker, MP for the Borough of Sheffield. Locke nevertheless gave priority to the Manchester end of the railway, serving more outlying settlements and thus offering earlier traffic potential at a

time when finances remained parlous. It must have helped that his choice of contractor for various sections of line was Thomas Brassey, a man with enormous drive and extreme skill in organisation. By the mid-1840s he had

Thomas Brassey, a leading railway contractor, was brought in by Joseph Locke to build parts of the Sheffield to Manchester line.

The impressive Dinting Vale viaduct showing the wrought-iron plate girders that in 1859-60 replaced the original and more attractive wooden arches. (Pendragon collection)

Sadly, the viaduct later lost its symmetry when the masonry pillars had to be propped up by unevenly spaced brick supports, as seen here in March 1977. (Gavin Morrison)

Woodhead station, opened in August 1844, looked more akin to a small prison in this bleak location. (Pendragon collection)

built one-third of Britain's railways and went on to construct lines throughout the world.

The first 8¼ miles from a temporary Manchester terminus at Travis Street as far as Godley were opened on 17th November 1841. Disgruntled shareholders nevertheless vented their displeasure that four years had now elapsed since the line had been sanctioned, their vehemence increased by completion eight months earlier of Summit tunnel and hence a competitive route from Sheffield. Passengers could take a connecting branch to the North Midland at Rotherham before travelling north to Normanton and thence over the Manchester & Leeds Railway.

Unhappy investors should have recognised that it was a roundabout 76-mile [122km] route where travel did not always go smoothly. Indicative that irony is not a recent form of satire was a brief report in the *Sheffield &*

Rotherham Independent under the heading 'Brisk Travelling'. It read: 'The passengers last Sunday evening by the quarter to five train from Sheffield reached their destination (Manchester) in eight hours. The train arrived at Normanton at the usual time, but had to stop there for an hour and fifty-five minutes. It then proceeded to Manchester, but so many were the stoppages that it did not reach that town until half-past twelve. Such are the inconveniences of this circuitous route.'

A long wait still lay ahead before opening of the Woodhead route, but a modest additional 1½ miles from Godley to Broadbottom were brought into use on 11th December 1842. Further progress east was briefly delayed by the 136ft [41m] high Etherow viaduct across the river gorge, its three laminated timber arches resting on piers using stone brought from nearby Tintwistle quarries. The

Woodhead – and its grim surroundings. Beyond is remote upland, where navvies lived in primitive stone huts for seven years to build the tunnel. Their work involved sinking deep access shafts, one of which is faintly visible on the moor top. (Biltcliffe collection)

foundation stone had been laid in March and by a remarkable achievement it was ready to carry its first trains on Christmas Day 1842.

These got as far as a temporary station preceding another viaduct still to be built before the line could extend any further. Much longer with five main timber arches and eleven approach brick arches, work on Dinting Vale viaduct started early in 1843. At its far side was a junction with the Duke of Norfolk's branch into Glossop. Completion of the viaduct enabled passenger services over another eight miles of railway through to a station at Woodhead, close to the western portal of the tunnel, to begin on 8th August 1844. The company recognised that one of the bleakest places in the country needed a licensed refreshment room where passengers could await connecting coach services into Sheffield.

Some of the more thoughtful of those seeking shelter and sustenance may have pondered on conditions endured by hundreds of navvies who had been toiling for more than five years on the still incomplete tunnel. Among them was a surgeon John Roberton, president of the learned Manchester Statistical Society, which was collecting data to improve the conditions of working people. He was both fascinated and appalled by what he found – and was determined to bring a change. At Woodhead he met another surgeon, Henry Pomfret, who gave graphic details of treating the injured. Further evidence of dire conditions came from a missionary, who kept a journal when sent to live with the navvies. At Summit tunnel these men had been mere shadowy figures, but now they emerged into sharp focus amid accusations culminating in an enquiry in Parliament.

Navvy life at Woodhead

The navvies were living in a scattered encampment stretching for over three miles across windswept moor above the line of the tunnel. Huts were roughly stone-built and had two rooms, one of which had a fireplace. As many as fifteen men would lodge in a single hut, often in filthy conditions that became a byword for squalor.

Twelve gangs of navvies were at work, two of them from each end of the tunnel. The others had to descend shafts that had taken upwards of two years to sink, with four of the five being over 500ft [150m] deep. Once at the bottom they worked in near darkness in opposite directions, blasting their way through a treacherous mix of gritstone, shale, slate and clay. The shafts were 10ft [3m] in diameter and the tunnel a constricted 15ft [4.5m] high and 18ft [5.4m] across. The men were struggling in mud that was generally ankle-deep and at worst could extend up to the knees. Parched by lack of air, they would resort to drinking a horrible-looking liquid running down the side walls. Small wonder that they suffered a condition akin to claustrophobia as well as chronic diarrhoea.

The surgeon Henry Pomfret was kept busy, going up to the tunnel two or three times a week in all weathers. Most of his time was spent operating on the broken limbs of men caught in rock falls. Other injuries were caused by carelessness in using gunpowder – one man had lost both his eyes and another had his arm broken as well as receiving severe burns to his face. The injured were patched up and left to recover in boiler houses at the shafts, which were the warmest places even if rain could often be dripping from the roof.

Pomfret gave depressing details to his fellow surgeon Roberton, alleging that 32 men had been killed and he had treated over 100 fractures, 140 other serious cases and some 400 minor injuries. He found it difficult to conceive a set of men more thoroughly depraved, degraded and reckless.

Part of the problem was that many navvies were drunk, especially following pay-day every nine weeks in a local pub. This would be followed by days of riot and rowdiness with men incapable of anything except fighting. Six constables employed to maintain order kept their distance. A constant cause of complaint was that beer was both more expensive and inferior to Manchester ale. It cost sixpence a quart (the present equivalent is about £2.20 per litre but there was then no chancellor adding tax to the price). The same grumble applied with food, which was only available at inflated prices from 'tommy shops' run by the contractor.

As was the case at Summit tunnel, the navvies were paid good wages with masons earning six shillings [£40] for a ten-hour shift and miners up to five shillings [£30] for eight hours of labouring. The contractor deducted three halfpence [60p] a day from every man to pay the surgeon and also a schoolmaster. The balance went into a sick fund, which provided a man with eight shillings [£40] a week when he was hurt or ill.

The company experienced constant difficulties in raising funds, but when successful it went ahead with construction night-and-day including Sundays. This shocked the superintendent of Manchester & Salford Town Mission into making two successive visits on the Sabbath, although the resident missionary took a more pragmatic view. He understood the need continually to pump water from the shafts but was distressed when blasting 'shook the school-house at the time when we were engaged in prayer at our afternoon meeting'.

The school was a short-lived venture and few children ever saw the classroom. Most were born illegitimate and were never baptised, although there was one strange exception at the nearby chapel of St James,

Woodhead. The curate entered the son of Henry Wilkinson and Martha Charlesworth in the register with his father being shown as a labourer. This was too much for the Church and it was presumably the vicar who struck out all reference to the father, added 'single woman' against the name of the mother and the abbreviation 'Ill' for 'illegitimate' in reference to the child.

In 1845 Roberton set down his findings in a pamphlet with the less than snappy title 'Demoralization and Injuries occasioned by the want of proper regulations of labourers engaged in the construction of railways'. The directors of the company were invited to its reading before the Manchester Statistical Society but did not attend. Instead they insisted that nothing improper had happened at Woodhead and were furious with Pomfret, accusing him of disloyalty in revealing details of accidents. Deaths were blamed on the carelessness of navvies, as instanced when one man stuck a candle in a barrel of loose gunpowder.

A robust response came from Thomas Nicholson, contractor for the greater part of the tunnel, in the form of his printed 'Strictures on a pamphlet published at the request of the Manchester Statistical Society'. He was angry that a missionary had been sent to a wilderness like Woodhead and stated that a horse would understand tunnelling just as well. Furthermore, Pomfret had exaggerated the number of deaths – there were in fact 26 – and also the extent of minor injuries by including men with scratched faces that they most probably got from their wives.

Naming names he described William Chadwick as 'one of the greatest blackguards that ever came to the tunnel', as he had drawn pay from the sick club for 18 months before being sacked for getting drunk and fighting. One George Wilson had leased some nearby land and brought up a number of loose women until orders were given that any men going there would be discharged.

Nicholson recited a long list of wholesome food he had provided as if to convince the world that his navvies had lived off nothing except the best. This included beef that he personally bought in Rotherham market and he also obtained genuine tobacco. Only two pubs could be used, but he had arranged for large amounts of malt to be sold so that the men could brew in the absence of any available milk. When a navvy died, he provided a good oak coffin at his own expense as well as dinner and a quart of ale for all those attending the funeral. Not mincing his words, he concluded that there never was a public work more respectably conducted, or with fewer depredations, insults or crimes committed by the workmen, throughout any part of England.

The *Manchester Guardian* was not convinced, commenting that a large body of people could not be allowed to live in a state of such fearful savagery without inflicting serious mischief upon society. It advocated a select committee to inquire into the condition of railway labourers and 'remedies which may be calculated to lessen the peculiar evils'.

The government of Sir Robert Peel was not unduly concerned and seemingly decided the best course was to set up a committee and then take no notice of its findings. It was a familiar tactic that has lasted to the present day. Over 3,000 questions were duly asked and all the failings documented in 200 pages of evidence. Navvies came across as drunken and perpetual rioters, while contractors fed their men on rotten food, got them drunk on beer and worked them seven days a week. Action was desperately needed but there was no public outcry and the report was not even debated.

Grand opening

A new era had already dawned at Woodhead. The tunnel was finally nearing completion and the line was opened from Sheffield through the growing market town of Penistone to a station at Dunford Bridge, close to its eastern portal, on 14th July 1845. Coaches took passengers and parcels over to Woodhead station until the end of the year when the great day at last arrived.

The *Sheffield Iris* could hardly contain itself: 'The tunnel is a wondrous triumph of art over nature and may be pronounced the greatest engineering work of its kind which has yet been consummated. So accurately was it driven from the faces under the calculations of the engineer that the bores met within a few inches, and so direct is the line of perforation that when standing at the eastern entrance we had no difficulty in observing daylight at the other end appearing like a small burning taper or a candlelight in a dark cupboard.'

Most of the navvies had now drifted away to find work on other lines, but some 300 still remained and on 22nd December were treated by the company to a celebratory feast on a scale previously unknown to them. It must have been something when the *Manchester Guardian* reported that there was more than they could possibly eat or drink, the fare including a huge bullock roasted on a spit constructed from surplus rails.

Every effort was made to ensure the same day's formal opening for the great and the good was very much a Sheffield occasion. A train of twenty carriages hauled by two locomotives, with flags flying and the yeomanry band in full blast, left the town's Bridgehouses station at 10.05am. Despite

There were few settlements between Penistone and the tunnel but this did not stop a station being built at Hazlehead Bridge. There was little sign of life when the staff and their families posed for this picture – and not surprisingly it closed as early as 1950. (Biltcliffe collection)

Dunford Bridge station, looking towards Sheffield. A very busy goods and stone yard is immediately beyond the up platform. (Biltcliffe collection)

a heavy fall of snow, it successfully reached the tunnel and all on board gave a hearty cheer on emerging at the far end a little over ten minutes later. No doubt they had mixed feelings of triumph and relief, as they were travelling on the first train through what was now the longest railway tunnel in the world.

Guests were welcomed at Manchester and the special then returned eastwards. It made an extra stop so that those on board could gaze with suitable awe at Dinting Vale viaduct. Sheffield was reached in time for a grand dinner lasting a full four hours with numerous speeches. The chairman John Parker summarised unparalleled difficulties that had beset the enterprise, struggles with impoverished finances, distrust of the public and doubts of shareholders. Using words that must have been carefully chosen, he referred to an excellently constructed railway from 'this great city of manufacturers – Sheffield – to that greater home of manufacturers and commerce which they had that day seen on the other side of the island'.

The heartiest of many toasts was 'Prosperity to the Sheffield, Ashton & Manchester', but many must have suspected that this had a hollow ring. Only seven months later the company had ceased to exist. Discussions with various proposed lines resulted in agreement to merge and form a single railway stretching from Manchester via Sheffield to Grimsby, where the port would foster traffic with Europe.

On 27th July 1846, Parliament gave its approval to a combined company called the Manchester, Sheffield & Lincolnshire Railway. Doubters soon averred that its initials stood for Money Sunk and Lost. When in later life it rashly decided to extend south to a Marylebone terminus in London and change its name to Great Central, it did not take long for dismayed shareholders to refer to their investments as Gone Completely.

The original single-track Woodhead tunnel soon caused long delays, which did not entirely go away when a second tunnel was opened. This view at Dunford Bridge shows one freight train buffered up to the guard's van of another, both waiting to head west.

Back at Woodhead

The new company had one immediate problem. Traffic between Sheffield and Manchester was increasing to the extent that the single-line through Woodhead tunnel was proving inadequate. Fear that two trains travelling in opposite directions might meet head-on had led to use of a patent magnetic telegraph as a primitive signalling system. In addition a single pilot engine, complete with a bright torch, had to be coupled to the front of every train. This ensured that only one train could ever be in the tunnel at any one time, but it all caused delays.

The decision to build a second parallel single-line tunnel was taken in 1847 and in theory it should have been much easier. Anticipating it might one day be required, twenty-five side arches had been provided at intervals in the original bore. These were

easily opened and it was not necessary to sink any additional working shafts. Lessons had been learnt regarding the welfare of those involved and the clergy in Penistone were given free travel to make frequent visits to Woodhead.

By mid-May 1849 there were 750 men working in three shifts night-and-day. All was going so well that they were given a week's holiday, when many went wild and drank themselves senseless. On returning, they developed what at first was thought to be dysentery but then others sickened daily and some died. A doctor diagnosed a sudden and violent outbreak of cholera – an epidemic that was sweeping the land. The *Manchester Guardian* insisted they had been guilty of 'the grossest imprudence and intemperance', which in modern speak means they were

Woodhead became notorious for the way smoke collected in the separate single-line bores, making conditions deeply unpleasant for enginemen and track workers. It can be seen oozing out of the right-hand tunnel as a Sheffield-bound express heads into the darkness. (Rixon Bucknall collection)

The same effect of lingering smoke is all too evident as a freight train emerges at Dunford Bridge. (Pendragon collection)

incapable of correct social distancing.

As more died horribly, the only medical remedy was regular meals and port wine. When more coffins were delivered in anticipation of need, most of the men fled and the place was virtually deserted. By the time they returned and the epidemic faded away, there had been 28 fatalities. It may have been fewer than feared, but it did nothing to lessen the evil reputation that persisted long after the second bore was completed in February 1852. The grim castellated portals added to a sense of foreboding.

Of all the great tunnels in Britain, Woodhead came to be regarded as the most difficult to work. Compared with the generous dimensions of the earlier double-track Summit tunnel, there was no space for smoke from steam trains to escape. Gangers struggling to maintain the track could scarcely find their way and in as little as six years many became invalids after contracting silicosis. Only when an attempt was made to handle more trains by opening a signal box inside the tunnels did men rebel at the atrocious working conditions and it had to be closed.

Generations of enginemen relied on handkerchiefs to avoid suffocation and often came close to collapse, especially with freight trains toiling up the 1 in 201 gradient towards Sheffield. The blast from the chimney rebounded against the walls, choking fumes and swirling ashes were everywhere and in the all-pervading blackness it seemed as if the proverbial light at the end of the tunnel would never be reached. Not without good reason did they condemn the dreadful three miles as the Woodhead hell-holes.

The castellated entrances at Woodhead were entirely appropriate for such a harsh setting. A final touch was the inclusion of sculptured gargoyles – a lion's head can just be seen on the left of the picture. (BICC)

4

Triumph in Huddersfield

Standedge Tunnels

Huddersfield station

'Railway Mania'

The 'railway mania' beginning in 1844 coincided with near completion of the Woodhead route, which in turn highlighted several major issues. Firstly, Sheffield was about to have a more direct link with Manchester than had Leeds, where the pending change in status was not welcome. The existing Calder Valley main line was all very well, but its roundabout route of 62 miles (99km) increasingly left much to be desired. Building a more direct railway of some 43 miles (69km) by tunnelling under the Pennine watershed at Standedge would also serve two major settlements bypassed by George Stephenson and still without adequate rail access.

The first was Dewsbury, expanding rapidly and becoming capital of the heavy woollen district thanks to the invention of shoddy by combing out rags. The town was only eight miles from Leeds but disgruntled travellers had first to head in the opposite direction for over a mile to a station on the main line. They then had to face a 21-mile (34km) journey via Normanton.

The second was Huddersfield, which helped by its two canals had become noted for producing fine worsteds as well as cloth caps for the working man. In 1844 it had a population of over 25,000 and was described by the noted political historian Friedrich Engels as 'the handsomest by far of all the factory towns in Yorkshire and Lancashire'. Yet it was badly placed in the railway age and its nearest station on the Calder Valley main line was three miles distant at Cooper Bridge.

The Manchester & Leeds Railway, sensing imminent loss of traffic, made a belated attempt to recognise the needs of Huddersfield. It proposed to build a branch line from Cooper Bridge along the floor of the Colne Valley to terminate in the lower part of the town. This would save costs but would rule out any possible extension westwards.

Hitherto it might have been a welcome development, but was condemned at a stormy public meeting in January 1844. Captain Laws, the company's general manager, was accused of a deliberate ploy to safeguard their existing main line. One speaker set the mood by perceptively commenting that the object was 'to clap us in a hole and keep us there', while another received great applause when he castigated the company as 'the most brutal in the whole kingdom'. The proposal got as far as Parliament but was abandoned in May when a more ambitious scheme received widespread approval.

From a junction with the Calder Valley main line at Heaton Lodge, 1½ miles west of Mirfield, the Huddersfield & Manchester Railway would climb more steeply but at greater cost to the centre of the town. From here it would parallel the Huddersfield Canal

The changing scene at the Huddersfield end of Standedge with a westbound Jubilee-hauled express about to enter the double-track tunnel. It is running alongside the canal, which greatly helped construction of the first railway tunnel. (Eric Treacy)

The same location in June 2001 with a three-car Class 158 providing the trans-Pennine service. A car park now serves a visitor centre. (Gavin Morrison)

towards Manchester and join other proposed lines at Stalybridge. At Standedge there would be a saving estimated at £70,000 [£7 million] by running alongside the existing canal tunnel, from where adits cut into arches in its side wall would save the toil of sinking shafts from the moor top.

Negotiations were now opened with the canal company. Keeping solvent had not been easy and many shareholders were probably relieved to sell out in May 1844 for as much as £183,730 [£18.5 million]. The combined enterprise, taking the cumbersome full title of the Huddersfield & Manchester Railway & Canal Company, depended on gaining approval in Parliament the following year.

A town with a difference

Huddersfield was in more than one sense a town apart. Other than a few small plots of land, it was still entirely owned by the Ramsden family – a state of affairs that was to last until as late as 1920. The family seat was at Byram Hall, near Pontefract, and the 4th baronet, Sir John Ramsden, was a true absentee landlord only visiting the town once during the 70 years he held the title. His main involvement was the annual rents totalling £85,000 [£7.5 million] and other matters were left to languish. He had little interest in railways as Huddersfield already had its canals. On his death in 1839, the baronetcy passed to his grandson John William Ramsden, aged only seven.

Trustees would now see the town through the turbulent years of the 'railway mania'. They were dominated by his mother, the Honourable Isabella Ramsden, known for her strength and intuition, and her first cousin and brother-in-law, the 5th Earl Fitzwilliam. His seat was Britain's longest stately mansion at Wentworth Woodhouse in the heart of a rapidly developing Barnsley coalfield. A powerful figure, his existing vast wealth was increasing by the week and together these two trustees made a formidable combination.

The Earl realised that the Ramsden estate would need to recognise the threats and opportunities posed by the coming 'mania'

and appoint an agent of high calibre. The choice fell on George Loch, an auditor of established reputation and also a trained lawyer. In true Yorkshire style there was concern regarding a 'large salary' of £600 [£60,500] for what was far from a full-time appointment but this was put to one side.

On taking up the post in July 1844 he was faced with a cascade of railway schemes seeking approval in Parliament in 1845 and all requiring Ramsden land. Apart from the Huddersfield & Manchester, he favoured a line connecting with it in the shape of the Leeds, Dewsbury & Manchester Railway. It would link the first two towns in its title and then run alongside the Calder Valley main line from Ravensthorpe through Mirfield to Heaton Lodge, thus playing its part in establishing a new direct route between Leeds and Manchester. He also welcomed the Huddersfield & Sheffield Junction Railway, heading south across the grain of the countryside to join the Woodhead route at Penistone. In each case the consulting engineer was Joseph Locke.

Other schemes, described by Loch as 'wild and insolent', included a line backed by the Manchester & Leeds Railway, which among other objectives sought to link Bradford with Halifax and Huddersfield. All now hinged on events in Parliament, where

Loch could display his adversarial skills. The venture that so severely troubled him passed the Commons but was thrown out in the Lords, where Earl Fitzwilliam may well have exerted considerable pressure. This could have extended to all three of Loch's favoured railways receiving parliamentary approval in April 1845 despite Board of Trade recommendations to the contrary.

Whatever may be the suspicions of underhand aristocratic influence, there can be no doubt about the great rejoicing when news reached Huddersfield on the morning mail coach. The *Leeds Mercury* enthused: 'The bells were instantly set in motion and the whole population rose from their slumbers, and music paraded the town. Mutual congratulations and rejoicings which spread to the villages around were the order of the day. Huddersfield has arisen. Posterity will remember this period with delight.'

It was certainly an extraordinary change in fortune. Only a year earlier it seemed that Huddersfield was going to be left behind in the railway age with no more than a mere branch terminus at the bottom end of the town. Now it was poised to enter a new era, as the midway point on a direct line connecting Leeds with Manchester and the junction for a cross-country link to Penistone and hence Sheffield.

The next twelve months were to be tangled and tempestuous in the extreme and the detail would not make light reading. In essence, the high noon of the 'railway mania' created a whirlpool of conflicting manoeuvres akin to pawns on a chessboard. Railways that existed in reality rather than merely on paper attempted to strengthen their position by determination bordering on desperation. Typifying them was a predatory move by the Sheffield, Ashton-under-Lyne & Manchester, seeking to expand towards Leeds and the North East. It came close

Huddersfield station, the pinnacle of determination by George Loch to create a 'new town' worthy of the position held by the Ramsden family. With full support from the locally-based Huddersfield & Manchester Railway, there arose a structure remarkable for a community with a population of less than 30,000. (Geoff Sheppard)

Wentworth Woodhouse, near Rotherham, famous as Britain's longest stately home. It was the seat of the 5th Earl Fitzwilliam, closely involved with the vision of a 'new town' for Huddersfield, who seemingly instructed his architect James Pigott Pritchett to design the station. It can only be surmised, but was Pritchett instructed to include a similar five-bay portico? (Dave Pickersgill)

to obtaining a lease of the Huddersfield & Manchester, finally rejected by a close vote of 4,088 to 3,475. According to one report, it was favoured by the chairman and MP for Leeds, William Aldam, but vociferously opposed by deputy chairman Joseph Brook, a local mill owner held in high esteem as 'the father of Huddersfield'. He reputedly left a seven-hour acrimonious meeting carried on the shoulders of shareholders when the lease failed.

A previously unthinkable development centred on the Huddersfield & Sheffield Junction Railway. It was absorbed by the Manchester & Leeds as part of an alliance with other companies to develop a through route from Bradford to Sheffield. Strenuous opposition and counter proposals became part of the course, but there emerged what came to be seen as a sensible compromise.

The Huddersfield & Manchester would grant running powers to its established rival. These would extend from the Calder Valley main line into Huddersfield, enabling it to connect with the Penistone line at a jointly operated station. In return, the new trans-Pennine route would share the existing main line between Ravensthorpe and Heaton Lodge rather than incur the expense of building parallel tracks. It was a remarkable outbreak of peace between two previously hostile companies.

George Loch was left with relatively minor problems, such as Isabella Ramsden insisting on a whim that the line leaving Huddersfield towards Manchester must be diverted to avoid Paddock church. She got her way. More serious was a failure to convince the directors that Standedge tunnel should be double-track so that the railway would be 'the best as well as the shortest between Liverpool and Leeds'. With hindsight Loch was undoubtedly right but was overruled due to what may have been pessimistic estimates. These stated that it would increase the cost from £25 [£2,500] to £47 [£4,600] per yard and take eighteen months longer to build, so it went ahead as a single bore.

Having been so successful in bringing railways to Huddersfield, Loch was now able to change tack. He was determined that the Ramsden estate and not railway shareholders should be the main beneficiaries of his involvement. As a canny Scot, he took a highly commercial stance and concentrated on extracting the maximum possible amount of money from the Huddersfield & Manchester for the land it would require. Unlike normal practice, the company was spared having to deal with countless small owners, but it still proved a protracted process. Negotiations completed in December 1845 resulted in £37,500 [£3.7 million] passing to the trustees and Isabella Ramsden personally receiving £3,000 [£293,000]. In addition, agreement was reached to sell Sir John Ramsden's Canal to the railway for £46,560 [£4.5 million]. Funds were now available for Loch to plan a 'new town' worthy of the required pomp with the station as its crowning glory.

With the full support of Joseph Brook, the Huddersfield & Manchester embarked on creating a station with few equals. It seems likely that Earl Fitzwilliam may again have played a key role by insisting that the architect should be James Pigott Pritchett of York. His was a practice that had acted for the Fitzwilliam estate for more than 30 years. The exact circumstances will never be known but Pritchett would be familiar with Wentworth Woodhouse and its giant five-bay portico with fluted Corinthian columns. The Earl, impressed by plans for Huddersfield, could well have asked for as close a match as possible and Pritchett would act as requested.

Although well short of the 600ft [180m] length of Wentworth Woodhouse, the station is still impressive enough with its 416ft [125m] façade. Built in sandstone, the design provided that the massive central 68ft [20m] high portico, reminiscent of a Corinthian temple, would on each side have nine-bay colonnades stretching away to a single-storey pavilion. It was a magnificent and monumentally classical concept. Internally the arrangements were much more modest with just a single 700ft [210m] long platform – a common approach with early stations and already adopted at Manchester Victoria.

The estimated cost was £14,100 [£1.4 million], although the accepted tender in June 1846 totalled £20,119 [£2 million]. It was from Joseph Kaye, owner of a huge and successful local building firm at one time employing over a thousand men. Earl Fitzwilliam laid the foundation stone on 9th October when the day was declared a public holiday and church bells rang out from early morning. Four months later, shareholders were assured that construction was 'proceeding very satisfactory', but it was a state of affairs that was not to last.

The carriage may be modern but the locomotive and its black livery certainly capture the atmosphere of the London & North Western Railway, which took over the Standedge line in 1847. Preserved Webb 'coal tank' No. 1054 is entering Diggle and returning to its then base at Dinting, August 1986. (Gavin Morrison)

Higher command

By early 1847 it was clear that small companies could not long hope to remain independent in depressed times following the sudden collapse of the 'railway mania'. Many shareholders were in desperate straits, as instanced when the Huddersfield & Manchester directors were accused of 'profligate and excessive expenditure, imbecility and harassing the proprietors with unnecessary calls on their shares'. Compared with the earlier rejection of a take-over, there was little resistance to an offer of five per cent on original outlay until the line was completed and thereafter seven-tenths of the dividend.

The bid came from the London & North Western Railway, formed in June 1846 as the largest system under single ownership. Stretching from the capital to Manchester, it saw an extension to Leeds as an important strategic acquisition and wasted no time. On 9th July 1847 the Huddersfield & Manchester and the Leeds, Dewsbury & Manchester were absorbed by what became known as the Premier Line. Legalities for the two canals

serving Huddersfield and already under railway ownership covered 'the correction or prevention of any inconveniences or evils'! On the same date the Manchester & Leeds became the Lancashire & Yorkshire Railway.

A new order was clearly evident when Henry Booth, joint secretary of the London & North Western, made his first visit to Huddersfield station and was shocked by what he found. Lying on the ground prior to erection were Corinthian columns for the colossal portico. Having no feeling of local pride and appalled by what he regarded as wanton extravagance, he ordered that work on the station should cease. Reputedly he went further by suggesting the pillars be carted away for use at the Greenhead home of Joseph Brook. The sarcasm may have been a mistake in securing support for a London-based company. Not for the first time in railway matters, Brook refused to be defeated and work eventually continued to the original design. Although there were further standstills, it must have helped that he had become a London & North Western director.

Construction of the new trans-Pennine main line was now well advanced, with priority having been given to the four-mile stretch from Heaton Lodge to Huddersfield in order to give the town rail access. Crossing a lengthy viaduct with 45 stone arches and two iron spans, it was opened on 2nd August 1847. Temporary arrangements were in force in a single wing of the station when Brook performed the ceremony. No longer the driving force behind a local company that had done so much for the town, he must have had decidedly mixed emotions.

The next stage to be completed under the guidance of its engineer Thomas Grainger was the eleven miles [17.5km] from Leeds through Dewsbury to the junction with the Calder Valley main line at Ravensthorpe. It included the 1 mile 1,609yd [3.07km] double-track Morley tunnel. Although not piercing the Pennine watershed, it was still a major undertaking and 18 shafts were sunk so that work could peak at 300yd [273m] per month. More than a quarter of a mile longer than Summit tunnel, it says much for the development of civil engineering that it had a shorter construction time by almost a year. This was despite problems occurring with the original contractors, who were dismissed when it was reportedly found that two fast converging sections were about to pass one above the other!

The double-track tunnel was completed in May 1848 but there were then problems characteristic of the times in general and Yorkshire stubbornness in particular. A local managing committee trying to maintain its independence to the last ran a formal opening train on 31st July but failed to notify the parent company of the ceremonies. The London & North Western board loftily declared that it did not recognise the line as open, only to be told by the committee it must do so from 7th August. This was blatant insubordination to a military man such as Captain Mark Huish, the company's militant general manager, who made a personal visit to Leeds and arranged an 'official' opening on 18th September. Refusing to be crushed, the committee told the board four days later that the two engines it had sent to run passenger services were 'unfit to work.'

Similar complaints were still being voiced in October. Finding a compromise was not helped by the fact that work on the Standedge line west of Huddersfield was still in progress and therefore the London & North Western could not in any event begin through passenger services. In what both sides may have considered a climb-down, it was eventually arranged that the Lancashire & Yorkshire would work the disputed line as if it were its own. On 1st December 1848 it began passenger traffic between Leeds and Huddersfield with trains serving the manorial-style Dewsbury station.

Although almost two miles long, Morley tunnel is distinctly second string to Standedge and lacks its dramatic setting. Its Leeds end is hard against the platforms of Morley station, seen here with Class 47 No. 47526 heading a Liverpool to York service in July 1979. (Gavin Morrison)

Standedge tunnel

Morley tunnel briefly held the accolade of the longest on the London & North Western. It clearly could not last as work was well advanced at Standedge on the single-track Nicholson tunnel, taking its name from the main contractor. Thomas Nicholson no doubt benefited from all the experience he had gained at Woodhead and was fresh from doing battle with the Manchester Statistical Society. The more civilised setting at 700ft [217m] as opposed to almost 1,000ft [310m] above sea level also helped, as was similarly the case with resident engineer Alfred Jee who had previously worked with Joseph Locke at Woodhead. His promising career was tragically cut short on a newly built line in Spain, when the locomotive he was driving toppled over and he was killed instantly.

There were few problems with the Standedge workforce, although a riot broke out at the British Queen pub in nearby Marsden when payment was delayed. A large force of police set out from Huddersfield by road to restore order and according to local lore unknowingly passed rioters heading in the opposite direction on the canal towpath!

As anticipated, the parallel canal tunnel proved its worth. Thirteen connecting adits enabled spoil to be taken out by barge and almost 2,000 navvies worked at 36 faces. Nine men died, which was a marked improvement on the 41 at Summit and 26 at Woodhead. Statisticians should note the use of 102 tons of gunpowder, 150,000lb (67.5kg) of candles and, more importantly, an initial estimate of £147,240 [£14.9 million] for the total cost with a final figure of £201,608 [£20.4 million]. The tunnel was complete by the end of January 1849 and thus had taken a little over two years compared with the seven gruelling years of Woodhead.

At 3 miles 62yd [4.88km] the new Standedge tunnel was shorter by 103 yards (94m) than its predecessor on the adjacent canal. This scarcely mattered, as in the superiority stakes it was 40 yards [36.6m] longer than Woodhead. Leaving aside the London Underground, it remained Britain's longest railway tunnel for almost another forty years until deprived of this distinction in 1886 when the Great Western completed its line under the Severn estuary.

It was unfortunate that rapid construction of both Morley and Standedge tunnels did not clear the way for immediate opening of the new main line from Leeds to Manchester. The hold-up was in Huddersfield where work had initially been delayed by uncertainty over junction arrangements with the Penistone line. The adventurous intention that it would be inside a tunnel was sensibly abandoned in favour of a deep cutting. Between the station and the junction there still remained a 685yd [623m] tunnel where poor preparation resulted in headings seriously out of alignment. Allegations were made of repeated tampering of pegs fixed at the bottom of shafts, which the navvies claimed was divine retribution on the directors for having reduced their wages! Local newspapers had much to say about bad workmanship, poor materials, incompetent management and general disarray.

Not until 13th July 1849 was it possible for a ceremonial opening to take place through Standedge tunnel when an enormous train of 29 carriages drawn by two locomotives and banked by a third left Huddersfield to cover the 17¾ miles [28.4km] to Stalybridge and thence Manchester. It surmounted a ruling 1 in 105 gradient up the Colne Valley and at the other side crossed the lofty and dramatically sited 22-arch Saddleworth viaduct. Through London & North Western services between Leeds and Manchester began on 1st August 1849.

As at Woodhead, a pilot locomotive normally provided safe working through

Springwood junction in Huddersfield where the Penistone route diverges from the four-track Standedge line heading off to the left. The original plans provided for the junction to be inside a tunnel but a wise change was to substitute a deep cutting. Jubilee No. 45558 *Manitoba* is in charge of a Leeds to Manchester local service in May 1959. (Gavin Morrison)

the single-line Standedge tunnel. A lapse in 1850 saw one of its drivers appearing in court for 'being found drunk and incapable but nevertheless had taken his engine through the tunnel and back again piloting trains'. He was sent to prison for two months with hard labour. The railway created a major growth of industry and mills all the way up the Colne Valley to Slaithwaite and Marsden, but there was never the same volume of westbound coal traffic as at Woodhead. It was 1868 before the London & North Western started work on a second single-line bore, named the Nelson tunnel after its contractor Thomas Nelson of

Carlisle. It was completed on 12th February 1871 at a cost of £121,500 [£11.4 million].

Standedge came to have the only four-track main-line through the Pennine watershed when an additional double-line bore was opened on 5th August 1894. Conditions for the workforce were now getting more civilised and 1,800 men lived at Diggle paper mills as well as in wooden huts close to the lineside. The earlier single-line tunnels survived until 31st October 1966 when they were closed after being used for tests in connection with the Channel Tunnel project.

A unique feature at Standedge was the

Saddleworth viaduct with the Pennine hills rising behind it. A Scarborough to Liverpool express is headed by Class 45 No. 45009, June 1983. (Gavin Morrison)

The Manchester end of Standedge with a very dirty No. 5003 about to enter the original Nicholson tunnel on a wintry day in January 1965. The large tank at the end of Diggle station platforms fed the water troughs immediately inside the tunnels. (Gavin Morrison)

provision inside the tunnels of water troughs, enabling steam locomotives to pick up this essential commodity via a tender scoop without stopping. The location was chosen because it was the only point between Leeds and Manchester with sufficient length of track both straight and level. It had the advantage that the troughs were less liable to freeze in winter. They were fed from a reservoir at Diggle built to supply the Huddersfield Canal, which in turn secured its place in transport history by reaching a deplorable state before closure in 1943. It compounded sceptics by reopening in May 2001 after a £5 million restoration project.

From the top:
Marsden signal box, close to the east end of Standedge tunnels. Its size indicates the volume of traffic on the line in its heyday. At extreme right is the all-essential coke stove.

One of the unique water troughs inside Standedge tunnels – the only suitable location on the Leeds to Manchester line where the track was both straight and level. (John Marshall collection – Kidderminster Railway Museum)

Lowering the tender scoop at the correct moment to pick up water was difficult enough in daylight but especially challenging inside a tunnel. These warning lights were provided at Standedge to indicate when approaching the trough. (John Marshall collection – Kidderminster Railway Museum)

The Penistone line left Huddersfield by crossing the spectacular Lockwood viaduct with its 32 arches towering high above the River Holme.

Back in Huddersfield

Last of the railways serving Huddersfield to be opened was the 13½-mile [21.5km] Penistone line on 1st July 1850. It had heavy engineering and on the outskirts of the town was the 136ft [41m] high Lockwood viaduct – one of the largest in Britain. It fully brought the Lancashire & Yorkshire Railway into joining the London & North Western at Huddersfield station, finally completed in October 1850 when a large clock was added to the portico by local clockmaker Richard Heslop. He was later given the job of repairing and maintaining all the company's timepieces north of Stafford.

Despite its magnificence, the station was not bestowed with an official opening ceremony. This may have been due to continuing ill feeling towards the London & North Western in a town where there was still high regard for the old order represented by

Joseph Brook. Might he have played a role in a mystery still surrounding the station? Stones carved with armorial devices surmount the end pavilions. At the Penistone end are the arms of the Lancashire & Yorkshire and the other ought logically to have been those of the London & North Western, thus representing the two joint users at the time of completion. Instead it is the far more obscure device of the Huddersfield & Manchester with a beehive alluding to general industry and a prophetic motto 'Devant si je puis' ('Forward if I am able'). Ceasing to exist in 1847 the company was certainly unable to move forward, but whether it was Brook, George Loch or another party determined to perpetuate its origins remains unknown.

Completion of the station immediately preceded an immense increase in rail travel due to the 1851 Great Exhibition – the ultimate symbol of Britain's colonial and industrial supremacy. It was a timely moment for Loch to move forward with his plans for a 'new town' extending from the spacious St George's Square in front of the station. The result was dignified new streets without parallel among northern industrial towns, thanks in large measure to the involvement of the leading Victorian architect William Tite.

The station was formally made the joint property of the two companies in 1862 when staff were issued with uniforms bearing HJS initials. Internally it little changed except that conditions became increasingly chaotic with the tunnel entrance hard against the west end of its single platform. Conflicting operations and shunting movements got worse as traffic increased with 140 passenger services and some 160 goods trains being handled on a daily basis in 1867. Almost another twenty years elapsed before an additional island platform was opened in 1886.

Another cause of frustration was separate ticket arrangements for the two companies in each of the end pavilions some 400ft (120m) apart. Many passengers missed their trains through choosing the wrong one and eventually the facilities were combined in a single booking office in the central portion of the building after it had seen use as a hotel.

The station grew old gracefully and by the late 1960s was becoming a sorry spectacle with 120 years of grime and the droppings from many thousands of pigeons. What now seems unthinkable was its proposed demolition 'for development', but it was a period that saw the demise of London's magnificent Euston terminus as well as Huddersfield suffering at a local level

The two end pavilions of Huddersfield station have coats-of-arms as their crowning glory. As might be expected, one is the arms of the Lancashire & Yorkshire Railway which was using the station on its completion in 1850. (Wikimedia Commons)

More surprising is the pavilion at the Leeds end with the arms of the Huddersfield & Manchester Railway & Canal Company. The motto, which translates as 'Forward if I am able', could be interpreted as a prophecy of pending doom. The company was taken over in July 1847, only nine months after the station's foundation stone had been laid. (Wikimedia Commons)

Opposite:
Above: The development of Huddersfield 'new town' was sufficiently far-sighted to leave a large open space in front of the station. The 416ft façade is difficult to portray in its entirety but here it is in more leisurely days before motor transport.

Below: The interior of Huddersfield station is insignificant when compared with the exterior. There was only a single long platform until 1886, when increasing congestion and delays led to opening of the island platform on the right in this image. In the distance is the tunnel taking the railway under the town to a junction with the Penistone line. (Gordon Biddle)

The continuous 1 in 105 climb from Huddersfield to Standedge was hard work for steam locomotives and thus a favourite stomping ground for the noted photographer Eric Treacy. This picture of a 'Black Five' near Marsden is one of many fine images taken on this stretch of line.

with imposition of a dual-carriageway ring road. Happily its station was saved and then had its exterior cleansed in 1972. A £4 million renovation was completed in 2009 when it won the Europa Nostra award for architecture. The writer Ian Nairn has succinctly described it as 'a stately home with trains in' and John Betjeman praised 'the most splendid station façade in England'. Supremely combining majesty and elegance, it is now recognised as the finest classical station in Britain.

Trains through the station have also radically changed from the days of steam-hauled Newcastle to Liverpool expresses faced with a heavy climb up to Standedge.

They now often start back at Edinburgh and are complemented by through services from Hull to Manchester Piccadilly. Workings on the Penistone line have been extended to Sheffield via Barnsley, but the biggest change stems from the period when Yorkshire's approach to air travel was as fragmented as had been the case with both canals and railways. It again enabled Manchester to soar ahead, this time in establishing the premier airport for northern England. As a result services from both Newcastle and Middlesbrough call at Huddersfield on their way to its integral rail terminus.

5

Midland Style

Totley and Cowburn Tunnels

Postcard of Totley Tunnel (Pendragon collection)

Glorious Latecomer

It says much for the extraordinarily rapid development of railways piercing the Pennines that three key tunnels were completed in just eight years. Summit, Woodhead and Standedge were all opened in the turbulent period from 1841 to 1849. There was a widespread view that there would be no more, as both Leeds and Sheffield now had direct rail access with Manchester. There would surely be no point in creating wasteful duplicate routes. More than thirty years rolled by without the position changing and it must have seemed that the challenge of building such tunnels had gone for good. One company saw it differently.

The Midland Railway was established in 1844. The North Midland line extending from Derby to Leeds joined forces with two other companies in the first large-scale amalgamation. For almost two decades it was content to remain a modest provincial concern based in Derby and relying on other lines to reach London and points both west and north. Then came the great renaissance driven by the dynamic Edward Shipley Ellis and James Allport, respectively chairman and general manager.

Their main goal was independent access to the capital, achieved in style in 1868 with the vastly magnificent St Pancras terminus and all the opulent splendour of its integral hotel. A year earlier it had extended west to Manchester, completing one of the most spectacular main lines in England cutting through the heart of the Peak District via Bakewell from Ambergate, north of Derby. It was utterly eclipsed in 1876 by the legendary Settle-Carlisle line, dubious in necessity and wondrous in execution. Within eight years the Midland had become an Anglo-Scottish trunk route.

Among these three great strides the Midland was also able to improve its access to Sheffield, still served by no more than a short branch line from Rotherham. The decision was finally made in 1864 to cut through hills south of the town that had so deterred George Stephenson. It was a pity it was left so late, as the entry into Sheffield involved the demolition of over a thousand houses – many of them newly built. Equally unfortunate, it was probably seen as a redeeming feature that they were occupied by what compulsory purchase powers described as 'the labouring class'.

The 13½-mile [21.6km] line from Chesterfield through the 1 mile 267yd [1.84km] Bradway tunnel was opened on 1st February 1870. There matters rested with the Midland taking stock after such a rapid period of expansion. It accepted an inability to compete with the Woodhead route for Sheffield to Manchester traffic as few passengers contemplated a journey via

931. "DORE & TOTLEY STATION."

Ambergate that was more than double the length.

The case to take action grew with the continuing expansion of Manchester, where a population of 827,000 in the 1871 census was soon to go over the million mark. A further incentive arose when the wheel came full circle and again brought innovation on a grand scale when it came to canals. This time it was the Manchester Ship Canal, largest of its kind in the world bringing ocean-going vessels into what became Britain's third busiest port. It was sanctioned in 1885 and opened nine years later – an achievement that recent experience with grand transport projects suggests could no longer be matched.

Increased trade for freight traffic with the 'city of steel' was clearly on the horizon and it was sufficient to convince Sheffield interests that an alternative to the Woodhead route would benefit more than just passengers. Incorporated in 1884 was the nominally independent Dore & Chinley Railway, which as indicated by its name sought to build a 20½-mile [33km] link between the Midland lines from Chesterfield to Sheffield and Ambergate to Manchester. It failed to raise sufficient capital and was about to be abandoned when the Midland decided at the eleventh hour to take over the venture. Apart from Sheffield-Manchester traffic, a

Dore & Totley station in its Midland Railway heyday. The passenger train from Sheffield is about to head into the 3½ miles of Totley tunnel. On the right are the Chesterfield lines that pass through Bradway tunnel.

Opposite:
Above: Special occasion at the east entrance to Totley tunnel shortly before its opening in November 1893. The contractor's locomotive *Nene*, built in Leeds by Hunslet, has its bunker decorated with flowers – 'DC' denoting the two extremities of the line at Dore and Chinley.

Below: Directors' inspection train pauses close to the east end of Cowburn tunnel for the locomotive *Cocker* to take water. The initials 'T' and 'O' are those of Thomas Oliver, contractor for the east half of the line.

Typical Midland Railway saddle tank used on major construction projects from the 1870s.

Midland elegance at Dore & Totley station about 1900.

Cowburn tunnel shaft is castellated and has an impressive depth of almost 800 feet. (Stephen Burton)

prime motive was an alternative route to its increasingly congested main line through the Peak District via Bakewell.

The southern end of the Pennine chain is split in half by the river Derwent and the Hope Valley, which meant two separate tunnels were required. From Dore the double-track line plunged into Totley tunnel, significantly longer at 3 miles 950yd [5.69km] than any on the existing trans-Pennine lines. It then ran up the valley to approach Chinley through Cowburn tunnel, a more modest affair but still 2 miles 182yd [3.37km] in length.

This was very much ducal country, which posed special considerations. The 7th Duke of Rutland, owner of much of the land around Totley, had a passion for shooting and obtained legislative provision that the number of tunnel ventilation shafts on his moor should be limited to one. Moreover, no construction work on it should take place between 10th August and 1st October in order

to ensure the sanctity of the 'glorious twelfth'. Finally, he insisted that it should not protrude above ground level otherwise it would disturb grouse in flight. The 7th Duke of Devonshire took a more positive attitude and specifically asked that a station be built at Hathersage in order to benefit local people.

The more heroic days of pioneering tunnel construction by relatively small local companies in the 1840s' heyday were over, but there were still challenges to be met. The main problem at Totley was the huge amount of water tapped by four permanent and three temporary shafts. It was vividly portrayed by a correspondent from the *Manchester Guardian* who visited the headings in December 1891: 'Every man seemed to be possessed of the miraculous power of Moses. Whenever he struck a rock, water sprang out of it … The flow became so constant that the men had to work in mackintosh suits and looked like divers wading through deep pools and

The slopes of Kinder Scout are in the distance near Edale as Class 170/6 No. 170637 forms a Liverpool to Norwich service, February 2007. (Gavin Morrison)

Jubilee No. 45598 *Basutoland* heads a Manchester to St Pancras express past Chinley South Junction, June 1957. The line to the right curves away towards Cowburn tunnel and Sheffield. (T J Edgington collection)

West end of Totley tunnel with its portal immediately behind the finely executed bridge to the hamlet of Padley. The untidy mess of working materials in the foreground would today be considered dangerous and was about to give way to Grindleford station. The photograph was taken in August 1893. (Gordon Biddle collection – Kidderminster Railway Museum)

Right: The woods above Totley tunnel form an attractive background to Grindleford station, which has just been passed by Freightliner Class 66/5 No. 66557 heading a westbound cement train, May 2004. (Gavin Morrison)

torrents.' It was especially bad at the western Padley end of the tunnel: 'The flow was so great the men had to go to work on a raft. Then the water rose so high that they could not go in at all without fighting a subterranean flood that almost rivalled the underground torrent Jules Verne evolved from his fancy.'

Excavations had more than once to be stopped for several weeks at a time with ten thousand gallons of water per hour being pumped from the headings. It helps to explain why the might of the Midland Railway still took over five years to build the tunnel, despite all the advantages of compressed-air drilling, boring machines for making shot holes, use of gelignite instead of gunpowder and availability of electric lighting. Although some finishing work still needed to be done,

East portal of Cowburn tunnel, which cuts through the Pennine watershed in a little over two miles. (Wikimedia)

the cost of the tunnel in September 1893 was put at £74 per yard – £461,000 [£51.5 million] in total.

It is fortunate the Midland had ample reserves, as the shorter Cowburn tunnel still cost an additional £270,200 [£30.2 million]. It required just a single shaft, one of the deepest in the country at 791ft [241m], which during construction flooded to the extent that men had to work in a diving bell. Only when the headings met could the water be pumped out to Chinley and sensibly used by locomotives.

Freight traffic on the line began in November 1893 but it was 1st June 1894 before passenger services commenced. A large volume of summer traffic was quickly established between Sheffield and stations in the Hope Valley, one of the most scenically attractive in the Peak District with nearby

Mam Tor – the 'shivering mountain' – as well as 2,088ft [637m] Kinder Scout and Blue John Caverns.

The destination for many travellers was the terminus at Manchester Central with its roof of 210ft [64m] span almost as impressive as St Pancras. The adjacent Midland Hotel, opened in 1903, could never hope to match its London namesake but still had 500 bedrooms, a winter garden, an 800-seat theatre and an early form of air-conditioning.

In a late improvement the Midland completed a new direct line into the centre of Manchester on 1st July 1902. Passing through the 2 miles 346yd [3.52km] Disley tunnel, it meant that almost eight miles of the journey from Sheffield was below ground. More significantly, the overall distance was now 45 miles [72km], only four miles longer than that via the Woodhead route.

6

Failure and Fire

Penistone station, May 1966 (John Marshall)

White Elephant at Woodhead

There was a grand finale to tunnels piercing the Pennines that promised an exciting future and yet ended in bitter disappointment. Traffic through the two Woodhead tunnels steadily increased in the heyday of railways and was directly related to development of the Barnsley coalfield. By 1875 its 55 collieries led Yorkshire output by producing 3.5 million tons of 'black diamonds' per annum, much of the fuel being moved west via Woodhead to meet incessant demand from Lancashire. From a giant marshalling yard at Wath-on-Dearne, coal traffic was worked up the steep 1 in 40 Worsborough bank to join the Sheffield-Manchester line at Penistone, which had developed as an important railway junction following opening of the line from Huddersfield in 1850.

With completion of a double-track tunnel at Standedge in 1894, Woodhead achieved an unfortunate distinction. It was now the only trans-Pennine route dependent on the grim confines of twin single-track bores to pierce the watershed. Understandably it

Penistone grew into an important railway junction and gained this new station in 1874. It was further transformed following introduction of the first electric workings over the Woodhead route from Wath-on-Dearne to Dunford Bridge in 1952. (Biltcliffe collection)

Best suit and tie plus white handkerchief in the top pocket look a touch incongruous as a high-powered delegation from the British Transport Commission visits the new single-track Thurgoland tunnel in July 1948. It allowed the original tunnel to accommodate overhead wires, which otherwise would not have been possible. (Pendragon collection)

remained as detested as ever by successive generations of enginemen. It was no comfort that conditions in the 220yd [200m] West Silkstone tunnel on Worsborough bank could be worse, with trains often requiring four locomotives and still coming to a halt if the rails were greasy. Respirators were provided on the footplate in special cupboards, which proved useful for storing the lunch packs of determined if stubborn crews who still opted for a handkerchief to keep out the smoke and fumes.

Two hours could be needed to cover the 19 miles [30km] from Wath to Dunford Bridge. There was a clear case for increasing line capacity and saving operating costs by electrification, which by the 1920s was widespread in both Europe and North America. In 1936 the LNER decided to electrify not just the Wath to Penistone line but also include the whole of the Woodhead route from Sheffield to Manchester. It would be the first such scheme in Britain for both passenger and freight traffic.

Halted by the Second World War, the project quickly restarted when peace was restored. October 1948 saw completion of a new 350yd [329m] single-track tunnel at Thurgoland, east of Penistone. It was built to enable the original double-track bore to be used solely for Sheffield-bound traffic and thus accommodate the 1,500 volt dc

Brief glory!

Top: Pioneer main-line electrification with a Manchester-London service emerging from the eastern portal of Woodhead tunnel on 18th June 1954 – fifteen days after its official opening. (Pendragon collection)

Lower: Electrified passenger services ended amid fierce controversy in January 1970. Two months later it seemed deeply ironic that diesel haulage was used for five special trains from Manchester to Sheffield for the FA Cup semi-final. Here is one of them passing Torside. (Gavin Morrison)

Work goes on day and night at Dunford Bridge to speed up construction of the new Woodhead tunnel, which took five years to complete and went way over budget. (D Ibbotson)

Opposite page:
Above: The scene at Woodhead in April 1954. The new tunnel is complete and platforms are being finished for the re-sited station. The two soot-grimed single-track bores are busy with traffic but would only see trains for another five months.

Below left: The new control room at Penistone was an integral part of the electrification scheme.

Below right: Formal opening ceremony at Woodhead on 3rd June 1954 by Alan Lennox-Boyd, Minister of Transport. Class EM1 Bo-Bo No. 26020 cut the opening ribbon with a special train. (Pendragon collection)

overhead wires.

Initially it was proposed to make space for wires in the existing Woodhead tunnels by lowering the tracks, but it became clear that a change of plan was needed. The constant pounding of steam locomotives had taken its toll to the extent that both the lining and mortar were rapidly deteriorating. Closing each bore in turn for nine months at a time to permit attempted repairs was creating chaotic traffic conditions and making little progress.

In November 1948 the newly formed Railway Executive took the radical step of sanctioning a new double-track tunnel. The construction contract was let to the noted firm of Balfour Beatty and three months later the hills around Woodhead again came to life with a workforce that soon numbered 1,100 men. The camp at Dunford Bridge was utterly different to its predecessor, with facilities including a cinema, hospital, shops, cafeteria and proper sanitation.

Modern machinery was expected to cut both the time and costs of construction, but it

did not prove that simple. The millstone grit through which three-quarters of the tunnel was driven proved to have such unpredictable shale that progress was reduced to a fraction of the intended rate. Then in 1951 two sections collapsed and halted much of the work for six months. Steel reinforcement ribs in mass concrete of 21-inch [53cm] thickness were eventually required and the opportunity was taken to ease future maintenance by providing permanent lighting and a mess room at the midway point.

Six lives were lost before the tunnel was completed in October 1953. It had maintained the tradition of its Pennine predecessors by taking far longer and costing much more than had been hoped. There was no lack of headshaking when the final figure came out at £4.25 million [£113 million] compared with a budget of £2.45 million [£65 million]. At 3 miles 66yd [4.89km], the new tunnel is 44 yards longer than its predecessors.

Initial electrification on 4th February 1952 was from Wath through Penistone to Dunford

Clsss EM2 Co-Co No 27000 at Sheffield Victoria on 14th September 1954 with a special train heralding the inauguration of electric services through to Manchester.

Bridge, thus enabling coal trains labouring up the notorious Worsborough bank to save as much as three-quarters of an hour on their journey time. Electric power gave way to steam for passage through the old Woodhead tunnels, which remained in use for a further two years.

Electrification was extended through to Manchester in May 1954 with Alan Lennox-Boyd, Minister of Transport, presiding at an official ceremony at Woodhead on 3rd June. The new tunnel never saw regular steam traffic and a final stage was inauguration of electric services from Sheffield on 14th September. It was a memorable occasion when a special train from King's Cross hauled by A4 No. 60008 *Dwight D Eisenhower* brought invited guests into Sheffield Victoria, there to be

taken forward by Class EM2 No. 27000 – one of seven Co-Co locomotives designed specifically for passenger work.

Reports of the return journey commented on an effortless climb of the 19 miles [30km] from Manchester to Woodhead in less than 24 minutes. Electrification of this demanding trans-Pennine route was regarded as a showpiece and among the greatest post-war achievements of British Railways.

The euphoria was not to last. At the opening ceremony the Minister of Transport had declared: 'All of us here believe that the railways have a future as important as their very great past.' It was soon seen as deep hypocrisy. With the nationwide decline in rail passenger traffic in the 1960s, attention focused on the necessity of two alternative

Staple traffic over the Woodhead route following electrification continued to be moving coal from South Yorkshire to Lancashire. Bo-Bo No. 26022 approaches Torside crossing in Longdendale as it returns with coal empties in September 1954. (Pendragon collection)

routes between Sheffield and Manchester. After fierce opposition, it was decided to withdraw services on the Woodhead line in favour of those via the Hope Valley. Protests were strongest from Penistone, bereft of rail access to Manchester when the proposals took effect on 5th January 1970. It was left with what became a service from Huddersfield to Sheffield via Barnsley operated by diesel multiple units.

Worse was to follow. Coal traffic steadily declined through the 1970s, gradually eroding the remaining purpose of the Woodhead route. Despite trade union pressure, it was resolved that its retention was no longer required. It was definitely a poignant moment in the early hours of 18th July 1981 when the

last freight train, hauled by a pair of electric locomotives, emerged from the tunnel. All that was now left of an electrification scheme once promising so much were suburban services from Manchester out to Glossop and Hadfield.

The tunnel still carries electricity in the form of high-voltage cables as an alternative to unsightly pylons in the Peak District National Park. It remains relatively dry and in good condition. In the new age of a 'Northern Powerhouse' and ever-increasing rail use, politicians from both sides of the Pennines frequently petition for a direct modern railway to link Sheffield and Manchester. Demanding that a new tunnel should be built, they do not seem to realise that one already exists.

A striking photograph of the new Woodhead tunnel, shortly after completion at a cost in today's money of well over £100 million. Understandably seen as a shocking waste of resources when abandoned after a working life of less than 30 years, it today remains forgotten by politicians who seek to impress by proposing a new tunnel to link Sheffield and Manchester. (BICC)

The sorry sight looking out of the eastern end of the tunnel in August 1986. The wires have been removed and the remaining track and overhead structures await recovery. Perhaps one day it may be re-used, completing another chapter in the saga of heroic railways piercing the Pennines? (Allan Trotter)

Summit Inferno

When the last freight train left Woodhead on a July morning in 1981, many must have expected that it would be a very long time before the Pennine tunnels again hit the headlines. They could not have been more wrong. Less than four years later the most spectacular drama unfurled in Summit tunnel – and came close to bringing its end.

All seemed well in the early hours of 20th December 1984 when a westbound freight entered the tunnel. It was headed by a Class 47, hauling what proved to be an unlucky thirteen tank wagons fully loaded with 835 tonnes of petroleum. Three-quarters of the way through, Driver Stanley Marshall became aware of a problem when his locomotive began to shudder violently. The train came to an abrupt halt. Climbing down from the cab together with Guard Graham Broadbent and Inspector Stanley Smalley, the three men peered through the dust and gloom to see what was wrong. Working their way back along the train, they did not have to go far. The third tanker was derailed and beyond it were wagons spread across both tracks in hideous confusion.

At that moment there was a flash and a loud 'whoosh' further down the train. Fire had broken out and was rapidly taking hold. Only too aware of what was being carried, the trio beat a hasty retreat and managed to leave the Littleborough end of

the tunnel unscathed. Guard Broadbent ran for almost a mile to the nearest lineside phone and alerted Preston power signal box of a potential catastrophe. Fortunately there were no other trains in the vicinity and all traffic was immediately stopped at the same time as Greater Manchester Fire Service was contacted. It was now 06.08am on a dark winter morning.

In a remarkable achievement the first fire pump arrived at Littleborough eight minutes later. Station Officer Robert Bonner described his initial reaction: 'There was a feeling that this was probably nothing serious. This view was reinforced when, on arrival at the tunnel entrance, there was absolutely nothing to be seen; no flames inside the tunnel, no smoke on the horizon, in fact not even a train! But, after climbing down the cutting to track level and being met by a distressed train crew, it was clear that something had happened.'

By 08.40 the severity of the accident was becoming apparent and the train crew were asked to return to the locomotive. The first three wagons were detached from the rest of the train with difficulty, their couplings having become too hot to handle, and brought out of the tunnel into a murky dawn. Close on 200 tonnes of petroleum were thus removed from what was now a deteriorating situation. Although fire crews wearing breathing apparatus had managed to control flames

The Summit tunnel inferno of 20th December 1984 at its most spectacular. Fierce flames from derailed tank wagons far below are roaring up the ventilation shafts and setting fire to surrounding moorland. (Manchester Evening News)

around several of the remaining wagons, the tunnel was filling with fumes accompanied by muffled explosions. As soon as some fires were extinguished, others fed by leaking fuel were relit. The blaze was soon out of control and a major incident was declared at 10.05am.

Events now turned awesome with biblical scenes above the tunnel as two tankers exploded and shook the hillside. Fireballs shot up the shafts high into the mountain air at over 100mph, scattering burning projectiles over a wide area and setting fire to vegetation. One eyewitness described the noise as 'like a jet plane taking off'. Amid real fears of a massive explosion, over 200 residents living in surrounding hamlets and farms were evacuated and the main Rochdale

to Todmorden road closed.

High drama continued throughout the day and it was the following morning before flames started to subside. Fire crews briefly re-entered the tunnel but reported loud and disconcerting noises – presumably caused by contracting metal, rock and brick. A second attempt that evening was abandoned due to extreme heat and further 'rumblings' deep inside. Not until Christmas Eve was the incident declared fully under control.

British Rail inspectors were granted entry on 27th December to assess the damage. They found both tracks buckled, some rails melted, sleepers destroyed and many of the tankers twisted beyond recognition. Temperatures calculated to have reached over 1,500 degrees

Having used foam to quell the initial blaze, fire crews work round a stricken tanker lying on its side. (West Yorkshire Fire & Rescue Service)

The intensity of the blaze was only too apparent when the fire was finally extinguished. Clearly visible are the twisted remains of a tanker, distorted track and damaged brickwork. (Greater Manchester Fire Service Museum)

centigrade had given the brickwork a glass-like deposit that appeared to flow down the walls. It was the worst ever tunnel fire in British railway history.

A public inquiry attributed the derailment to a 'catastrophic failure' of the axle bearing on one of the tankers. Made only too clear were the potential consequences had the train been carrying a nuclear load instead of petroleum. Determining if and when the tunnel could be repaired had to wait until charred wreckage of the tankers could be cut into small pieces and removed on trolleys over a three-month period.

It was soon found that decisions made by George Stephenson almost 150 years earlier had proved their worth. He had specified six courses of bricks to line the tunnel, prompting his resident engineer Barnard Dickinson to claim that it would defy the rage of fire. He was right. The outer course had perished in the inferno and fallen away, the second was severely damaged but the other four were unaffected.

Although the cost was estimated to be in excess of £1 million, work began on removing damaged brickwork, bracing two ventilation shafts, replacing cable signalling and laying a new double track. On 17th August an end-to-end walk through the tunnel was organised by Todmorden Rotary Club and two days later came a ceremonial reopening when dignitaries gathered at the town's station. A passenger train broke through a tape before passing under a celebratory arch of water, aptly provided by West Yorkshire Fire Service. It was a suitably dramatic and pivotal moment in the stirring story of heroic railways piercing the Pennines.

Sources and Further Reading

Much of the content of this book derives from research when writing *A Regional History of the Railways of Great Britain: Vol 8 South and West Yorkshire* (2nd edition, 1984). Sources included company minute books, Acts of Parliament and contemporary newspapers. This series is regarded as having stood the test of time. Railways on the Lancashire side of the Pennines are covered in *Vol 10 The North West* (Geoffrey O Holt, 1978). A helpful statistical summary is *British Railway Tunnels*, Alan Blower (1964).

Industrial Revolution

On waterways, the definitive work remains *The Canals of North West England*, Charles Hadfield & Gordon Biddle (2 vols, 1970). There have been several recent books on the Bridgewater Canal, but one of the best is still *Bridgewater: The Canal Duke 1736-1803*, Hugh Malet (1977). Wide-ranging studies of this crucial period are 'The First Industrial City: Manchester 1760-1830', Peter Hall (in *Cities in Civilization*, 1998) and *Industrial Revolution in Yorkshire*, Fred Singleton (1970).

The Railway Age

Recommended among the huge number of titles are *The Railways of Britain*, Jack Simmons (3rd edition, 1986) and the more recent *The Railways: Nation, Network and People*, Simon Bradley (2015). Important earlier works include *The Railways of Great Britain and Ireland*, Francis Whishaw (1842, reprinted 1969) and *The Railway Mania and its Aftermath*, Henry Grote Lewin (1936, reprinted 1968). Among the most readable of biographies is *George and Robert Stephenson: The Railway Revolution*, L T C Rolt (1960). At a regional level there is the Manchester chapter in *The Impact of Railways on Victorian Cities*, John R Kellett (1969).

First Line through the Pennines

Summit Tunnel has its own book locally published in Littleborough and deserving to be better known – *A Pennine Pioneer: The History of Summit Railway Tunnel*, Allen Holt (1999) is especially strong on construction details. The Manchester & Leeds Railway is similarly well served by *The Eleven Towns Railway*, Jeffrey Wells (2000). It includes A F Tait lithographs originally published in *Views of the Manchester & Leeds Railway* (1845, facsimile reprint 1971). The definitive company history is *The Lancashire & Yorkshire Railway*, John Marshall (3 vols, 1969-72). A highly praised local work is *Hebden Bridge and the Railway in the Nineteenth Century*, David N Taylor (2019).

The Woodhead Hell-Holes

Great Central, George Dow (3 vols, 1959-65) is outstanding among company histories. Woodhead has its own chapter in *The Railway Navvies*, Terry Coleman (1965), widely regarded as the classic work on the subject. There is similar coverage in *Joseph Locke: Railway Revolutionary*, N W Webster (1970).

Huddersfield and Standedge

Again it is fortunate that there is a good company history in the shape of *The London & North Western Railway*, M C Reed (1996). There is also *The Yorkshire Lines of the LNWR*, Neil Fraser (2019), which largely takes a year-by-year approach. Two now scarce booklets by Stanley Chadwick are 'All Stations to Manchester': The Centenary of the Huddersfield and Manchester Railway and Standedge Tunnel* (1949) and *Railway Wonder: Development of a Town* [Huddersfield] (1984). A unique feature is covered by Geoff Brown in 'Standedge Tunnel Water Troughs' (*Backtrack*, January 1996). Works giving high praise to Huddersfield station include *Railway Buildings of West*

Yorkshire 1812-1920, George Sheeran (1994); *Britain's Historic Railway Buildings*, Gordon Biddle (2003); and *Britain's 100 Best Railway Stations*, Simon Jenkins (2017). For the influence of the Ramsden family see *Power in the Land: The Ramsdens and their Huddersfield Estate*, edit Edward Royle (2020) and also an important paper 'A Landed Estate and the Railway: Huddersfield 1844-54', Dennis Whomsley (in *Journal of Transport History*, September 1974).

Midland Style

A detailed 300-page work forms the first part of a projected three-volume account of *The Hope Valley Line: Dore to Chinley*, Ted Hancock (2019). A more concise approach is taken by *Totley and the Tunnel*, Brian Edwards (1986), setting its subject in the context of its affect on the local community.

White Elephant at Woodhead

Events up to 1954 are covered in *The third Woodhead Tunnel*, George Dow. More recent information including re-opening proposals is on: forgottenrelics.co.uk/tunnels/Woodhead.html

Summit Inferno

A dramatic portrayal by Mike Bunn in 'Inferno under the Pennines' (*Backtrack*, December 2014) gives special emphasis to the role played by firemen. There is also 'Summit Tunnel – from fire to ice', Paul Stephen (in *Rail 797*, March 2016).

Acknowledgements

Many have offered help and inspiration over the long half-century since railways heroically piercing the Pennines first fascinated me. They have tolerated my jibes about the superiority of Yorkshire over Lancashire and part of the purpose of this book is to seek forgiveness. In putting research in perspective and locating suitable illustrations I have received help from Gordon Biddle, Michael Blakemore (publisher of *Backtrack*), Rob Bonner, Mike Bunn, Roger Carvell, Jane Houlton, Barry Lane, Chris Leach (Information Officer, Lancashire & Yorkshire Railway Society), Gavin Morrison, David Postle (Kidderminster Railway Museum) and Malcolm Preskett (Railway & Canal Historical Society). My wife Judith has again given every encouragement and Shep has been a constant companion.

Index